WATER

Peter Briggs

WATER

THE VITAL ESSENCE

HARPER & ROW, PUBLISHERS

New York, Evanston, and London

LIBRARY OF CONGRESS CATALOG CARD NUMBER: 67-11347

C-T

Contents

Sixteen pages of black-and-white photographs appear after page 116.

Preface

THIS book is all about man's relationship to water; fresh water, salt water, rain, snow, and ice. The relationship is one of the most contrary, paradoxical things in nature. Human beings are, physically, mostly water; they cannot live without it; yet water manifested as floods, hurricanes, and storms at sea is often fatal to man. The oceans can be hiding places for the nation's enemies, but they also provide great stores of fish and great lakes of oil can be tapped from their beds. Water can be beautiful and refreshing but it can also carry diseases such as cholera and bilharzia. Clams and oysters thrive in the seas but so do sharks and barracuda. The contradictions are endless.

The book itself was generated from an increasing awareness of several water-related stories that have been developing over the last few years. One of these is the growing science of oceanography, a field full of adventure and promise for the human race. Another is the water pollution story, which seemed to me, as an indignant American, in need of maximum exposure. Somewhat related is the problem of water supply in a nation whose population will double by the end of the century.

It took very little study to see that ultimately these things all tie in together. They have one common denominator.

The sea is the source of our weather and rainfall, and if the weather is to be modified, droughts and hurricanes controlled, it will have to be done from the sea. The sea is also the ultimate dump for all the pollution done to fresh water. Only the oceans can provide the material that may finally have to be desalinated for our seacoast cities.

Further study produced a number of other water stories which all bear on one another. Flood control dams and soil conservation measures deprive ocean beaches of sand, for example; indiscriminate pumping of fresh water near the seacoast permits salt water to intrude on the water table; fertilizer washed off farm lands causes lakes to grow luxuriant beds of weeds; on the other hand, deep-water drilling in the sea bed of the Continental Shelf for oil may produce enormous reserves of fresh water for nearby lands.

Finally, the book developed into a survey of the entire water situation in the world today. The emphasis is on the problems and opportunities of the United States, but water respects no boundaries, and the principles of water management are basically the same for every nation.

Such a commonplace thing as water has turned out to be not a very simple thing at all.

A list of all the kind people who helped me in this study of water would resemble a page in the Manhattan telephone directory. Rather than have such an uninteresting page (and run the risk of leaving someone out) I want to thank, all together, the hundreds of specialists in various fields who gave me so much time and information.

My appreciation also goes to the learned institutions of Lamont, Woods Hole, Scripps, New York University, the Hudson Laboratories of Columbia, Johns Hopkins University, and the universities of Rhode Island, Miami, Oregon, Washington, and Hawaii. In the field of government I am indebted to the Metropolitan Water Board of Los Angeles, the state conservation departments of New York and Minnesota, the water authorities of New York and Philadelphia, the Ohio River Sanitary Commission and the Tennessee Valley Authority. In Washington, my thanks go to several Congressmen and the more than thirty divisions of the executive branch concerned with water, particularly the Public Health Service, NASA, the various sections of the Department of the Interior, the National Science Foundation, the Smithsonian Institution, the Army Corps of Engineers, the Coast Guard, the Navy, and the Interagency Committee on Oceanography. Many industries concerned with water gave me valuable assistance and I hope I have dealt fairly with all of them.

Lastly, my thanks go to the New York Public Library and the *New York Times,* the best collaborators a researcher ever had.

P. B.

New York City
January, 1967

We are tied to the ocean. And when we go back to the sea—whether it is to sail or to watch it—we are going back from whence we came.—JOHN F. KENNEDY

1

A Happy Cosmic Accident

WATER is a chemical freak, an absolute necessity, a frightening phenomenon, a benevolent friend. It is abundant, yet frequently scarce. Physically the universal solvent, it at the same time pervades almost all of man's activities—politics, agriculture, industry, forestry, fishing, domestic tranquillity, and foreign affairs. Always utterly essential, water can no longer be taken for granted. Polluted and wasted since mankind took over the world, water is with terrible slowness being acknowledged to require very intelligent handling in the future if our race is to survive.

Whoever mistreats water does so at his own peril. This is as true in New York City as it is in the deserts of the American Southwest, as true in water-rich Minnesota as in the cholera-ridden slums of Calcutta. Because the population of the world is wildly increasing, water must be cherished, saved, treated with the reverence some people give only to money.

What most people know about the substance is that they are helpless without it. A person can go without food for a week, but he will die in three days without a drink of water. A city, it is now realized, can survive patiently overnight without electricity; yet if all the water, including that to hospitals, were cut off for only twelve hours, there would be panic. And it became a distinct possibility for a while that the reservoirs of the largest city in the Americas would become completely dry.

Beyond the problems of survival, the waters of the sea have become areas of great scientific, economic, and military interest. Spurred by such discoveries as the gigantic mountain ranges under the oceans, by the adventures of such explorers as Captain Jacques-Yves Cousteau, by the submarine challenges of World War II, the new science of oceanography has begun to flourish. Less well known to the public, but equally important as an incentive to study, is the recent proclamation of many countries, including the United States, that each seaboard nation owns the bottom of the sea out to the edge of the continental shelf in 600 feet of water. As sheer territory, this acquisition outranks for the United States the Louisiana Purchase and opens a new realm for exploration that calls for men of the breed of Lewis and Clark.

Already so complicated that when a new international textbook on the subject was begun a few years ago no man felt competent to write it by himself, oceanography combines practically all the sciences known to man—even psychology—applying them to what is often called "the hostile environment."

Yet many men feel at home in the sea. To them it is the last frontier on earth, a challenge to human intelligence and courage.

The seas, the rivers, the lakes and streams, the air around us . . . all act, react, and interact on one another, and all these things are crucial to man and his planet.

This book is to be not a scientific treatise—though science is part of its subject—but a reporter's account of the entire present-day situation and a discussion of the amazing facets of what is undeniably "the vital essence."

Why Is Water so Priceless?

You can exaggerate the value of many things, but never the value of water: it is impossible to attach too much worth to the colorless liquid most Americans get simply by turning on the tap. Not a plant or an animal or a pretty girl can exist without it. The bodies of young people are 90 per cent water, and, though the volume slowly diminishes to 75 per cent as people age, it still must be continually replaced.

Why Has the Water Supply Suddenly Become News?

We all know that we get thirsty, that animals must drink, that plants wither and die without moisture, and that water is essential for household use. This is all so obvious that it may well be asked, "Why labor the point?" The answer is that unless people understand now what is happening to the most important national resource, they may find it dismally unavailable in the not too distant future. This is not being unreasonably alarmist. By 1980 the water requirements of the United States are expected to amount to 600 billion gallons a day; but the maximum amount that can be developed, according to engineering estimates, will be 515 billion gallons. This leaves an apparent deficit of 85 billion gallons of water for every day of the year.

This is not quite so bad as it sounds because the water will be, as it frequently is even now, re-used many times on its way to the sea. But the situation is already tight enough to call for very careful handling.

Water is not suddenly disappearing. Because it is indestructible, there is as much now in the world as there ever has been. The trouble is that, with a static amount available, only so much rain can be expected to fall. Meanwhile, consumption by individuals, factories, and farms increases.

There is little danger that people will die in the United States for lack of water; the human body needs only five or six pints a day, and much of this can be absorbed by way of so-called solid food. What is in danger is the affluent American way of living, in which so much water goes to waste. Even so, people use only 10 per cent of the water supply directly on themselves—the rest goes to industry and agriculture. That is where suffering could arise: human beings will survive, but their comfort and happiness may be at stake.

What Makes Water so Special?

It is observed in the Van Nostrand *Scientific Encyclopedia* that "The role of water in our universe is on a par with, if not surpassing, that of any other known substance." Why is this true?

Men with orderly minds have tried to fit water and its infinite variety into neat compartments known as sciences. One of these compartments is geology, which begins by trying to explain how water originally came to be.

According to the Bible, the Lord created the earth, then the waters, and only then the dry land. This sequence of events is agreed to by many geologists, though they believe it all took not a few days but billions of years. It is generally believed that there was no water on our planet when it was formed, but that the chemicals to make it were present. Just how hydrogen and oxygen got together in such quantities is the subject of many theories, though no one theory claims that anything has been "proved."

Those who thought about the question in the Middle Ages believed that the water in the rivers flowed magically from the center of the earth. They did not believe that rain was responsible, because they observed that rivers could flow even when no rain had fallen for weeks. What was not understood at the time was that rivers continued to run because they were fed by ground water, the supply that accumulates below the surface from rain that has already fallen.

The theory most generally accepted today is that our newly formed planet originally had an atmosphere made up of carbon dioxide and ammonia, the latter being a compound of nitrogen and hydrogen. Water is thought to have first appeared on the surface as steam from molten lava—so much steam that torrential rains poured from the skies, perhaps for thousands of years. This theory seems plausible to anyone who has seen steam rising from a single volcano or a geyser; it is disputed, however, by those who say the steam is merely overheated ground water. Like the question of the origin of the earth itself, the problem of how water first got here will keep scientists happily puzzled for a long time.

Recent photographs of Mars appear to prove that there has been no erosion, and therefore little or no water, on that planet. If so, the earth may be unique: the only planet with a favorable balance of gaseous, liquid, and solid forms of water—a happy cosmic accident essential to life as we know it.

Water's Chemical Properties

The true chemical nature of water was discovered twice, and almost simultaneously, in the year 1781, by a Frenchman, Antoine Lavoisier, and an Englishman, Henry Cavendish. Both men demonstrated that two atoms of hydrogen combined with one atom of oxygen to make the fluid, a fact expressed in the well-known formula H_2O.

In recent years the concept has had to be modified with the discovery that both hydrogen and oxygen have isotopes, substances that are alike in every respect except their weight in atoms. One of these isotopes has been called deuterium. Twice the atomic weight of hydrogen, it combines with oxygen into "heavy water" and, as such, was crucial in the development of the first atomic bomb. Today it is believed there are sixteen possible formulas for the chemistry of water.

Absolutely pure H_2O is a "laboratory curiosity." In a state of nature water always contains traces of other elements. In the open sea it contains an average of 3.5 per cent NaCl, or salt. In the Red Sea the amount rises to 5.5 per cent while in the Baltic it is only .5 per cent. In addition, the sea contains all the elements there are in the world, if only in trace amounts.

When the Greeks of 2000 years ago wondered why the sea was salty, they came up with the answer that the salt must be made by the sun, for they had observed that if you left a pan of sea water out in the sun, only salt was left after exposure to its rays.

Today the accepted explanation for the chemical composition of the sea is that its salt content, and all its other mineral elements, have been washed away from the land by rain over billions of years. This alteration of the chemistry of the sea has, of course, had extremely important consequences for man.

Although it is widely believed that all life evolved out of the sea, modern man cannot drink sea water, even though the earliest animal species must have been able to do so. What happened is that the sea changed, while creatures using the fresh water on land did not need to change with it to survive. (The chemical composition of the human body has about the same proportion of the elements as sea water. The differences, though slight, are still enough so that men have cried, "All that water and not a drop to drink!")

Man has still not left the sea entirely, however, and along with other elemental requirements, he must have about two grams of salt a day. Even though the body does not retain salt in the digestive system, salt is essential for a number of metabolic processes and for the production of the hydrochloric acid necessary for digestion. The salt cellar on the table is a symbol of man's bondage to his evolutionary past.*

Pure fresh water is tasteless, colorless, and odorless—so without character that the public would complain if the authorities supplied it to them. In fact, the water in our faucets always has some trace of foreign substances, the most common being calcium carbonate, the ingredient that makes water "hard."

The Unique Properties of Water

Water in the solid form of snow is made up of countless trillions of icy particles that never exactly repeat the same pattern. Water in the solid form of ice is the only substance in the world that expands when it freezes. This is inconvenient to the owner of a car when the radiator freezes and bursts. If frozen water did not expand, however, it would not float in liquid water, and the world would long ago have become nothing but a gigantic ball of ice. For icebergs that had broken off glaciers, and the ice that flowed into the sea from rivers, would have sunk instead of floating at the surface where the sun or warm currents could melt them; each winter would have added new ice to the bottom of the sea. At great depths the water is only a few degrees above freezing, and its temperature would certainly have been reduced if great amounts of ice were continually added.

Water also behaves curiously in relation to heat. Compounds very similar in chemical structure boil at a temperature of 100° *below* zero. Water, at sea level, continues to absorb heat without boiling until a temperature of 212°

* The word *salary* comes from the Latin word for salt. Barbarians would not accept money as pay for service in the Roman army, but they would accept salt—whence, too, the remark that a man is "worth his salt."

above zero has been reached. This ability to absorb so much heat explains the complaint that "a watched pot never boils." If water were composed just a bit differently, all the liquid on earth would long since have boiled away into space.

The heat-absorbing quality of water explains why Florida, a peninsula in the sea, has a moist and balmy climate, while the Sahara, remote from the water, is hot as a furnace. The two are at the same latitude and receive a comparable amount of sunlight; but, while there is no water near the African desert to take up the heat, Florida is surrounded by water and also has the advantage of the Gulf Stream, which providently carries much of the heat north and east to far-away Great Britain and Norway. (Labrador and Greenland, at the same north latitudes but without the moderating effect of the Gulf Stream, are almost frozen solid.)

Another unusual property of water is its surface tension, the greatest among all ordinary liquids. Surface tension is the ability of a fluid to adhere to itself or to another substance. It causes water from a faucet to form drops rather than spray. Water adheres to solid substances, such as rocks and soil, and this is the principle behind the formation of ground water.

Another remarkable property of water is its ability to dissolve many other substances. It is the nearest thing there is to a universal solvent. Thus water in lakes, rivers, and oceans is really a solution of various substances with which it has come into contact. Water's ability to dissolve, and decompose, organic wastes is the reason that it is used everywhere as the base for disposing of them.

Water moves from liquid to gas to solid, and back again, with perfect ease. It is seldom changed chemically by all the things it carries. When it becomes a gas—that is, when it evaporates—by some process not at all well understood it sheds most impurities, such as salt, silt, and bacteria. If it did not do this, if water could be made permanently dirty, life would have been impossible on earth long ago.

Because of its power as a solvent and its ability to clean itself, water has been able, up to now, to carry all the load that man and nature have placed upon it. What it could not take care of immediately, it transported to the sea, the final depository for all the processes that took place on land.

The Hydrologic Cycle

The sea is a marvelously large thing to contemplate. Imagine, if you can, a cubic mile of water. A mile high, a mile wide, a mile across, it would stand four times as high as the Empire State Building. There are 139 million such units of water in the sea. The sea covers almost three-quarters of the surface of the earth and is about seven per cent of the earth's total mass. Such an amount of water is, of course, crucial in the constant flow around the earth that is known as the hydrologic cycle. Since, as a compound, water is essentially indestructible, it may be said that Cleopatra's bathwater is still somewhere in the world, carried by the self-perpetuating system that takes the water up from the earth's surface into the atmosphere, circulates it by means of all the variables of weather, then returns it to the earth in some form of precipitation.

The hydrologic cycle is, in technical language, a heat exchange system. It has also been described as a vast system of natural plumbing. As the water is evaporated by the energy of the sun, it is also purified. When it finally returns to the surface of the earth, most of it is soon evaporated once again. The water taken up by plants is transpired—that is, returned to the air as vapor through the leaves. Some of the rest of the precipitated water stays in lakes or becomes ground water.

The remainder is carried by gravity down streams and rivers to the sea, where the whole cycle starts again.

Meteorology

Just where and when precipitation occurs is a result of all the many forces that affect the weather. The sun does not vaporize water from all surfaces to the same extent. There is less evaporation when the sky is cloudy. There is less in winter than in summer. There is more evaporation at the Equator than at the North or South Pole. Such variables as these are the concern of the science of meteorology. Its name comes from the Greek word *meteora,* meaning "things in the air." Clouds, rain, sleet, and snow all fit the description, and are studied by meteorologists.

Water is important to meteorology because of the conservative way in which it reacts to heat. By day the rays of the sun warm it much more slowly than they do the land, and by night the land cools more quickly. Thus the breezes are toward the sea, whose surface temperature is now warmer by comparison.

The operation of many such unequal forces causes the air to circulate constantly, aided and abetted by the motion of the earth itself. As air moves higher, forced up by cold air from below or perhaps by an obstruction such as a mountain range, it encounters less pressure from the thinner atmosphere, and accordingly cools and begins to lose its capacity to hold water vapor. As it is released, the vapor may condense around a particle of dust or of salt thrust into the air by sea spray, to form a droplet, and then another, and so on into uncountable billions. These then may become a cloud, a vast reservoir of energy drawn from the sun, no longer in the form of heat but of electrical charges which may be released as thunder and lightning. Triggered by a mechanism that is not yet completely understood, the droplets may condense, freeze, or crystallize so as to reach the earth as sleet, hail, snow, or rain.

Meteorological researchers are, of course, interested in finding the causes of events such as hurricanes and typhoons. They are also interested in such apparently simple questions as where rain originates. It was long supposed that the moisture in the air of a particular region was primarily the result of evaporation from bodies of water or transpiration from plants fairly close at hand. Therefore it was supposed that rainfall in an area could be increased by planting forests so as to release a greater amount of water into the air. During the droughts of the 1930s a number of forests were planted with this in mind. An elaborate experiment has now shown, however, that for the eastern third of the United States about 90 per cent of the clouds that produce rain are formed over the Gulf of Mexico. Rain-making by planting trees is apparently a hopeless endeavor.

How Water Reshapes the World

The hydrologic cycle is continually changing the face of the earth. As peaceful rain, it nourishes the green farms and forests. In the violence of hurricanes, it smashes and destroys what man has built. Unobtrusively, but incessantly, it eats away continents. The greatest mountains are slowly ground down into hills by little drops of water and by great grinding glaciers. Often as a result of man's poor farming methods, topsoil is washed out to sea. Half the topsoil available in the United States in the days of George Washington has now been rained off the land.

Visually the world's most spectacular example of water at work is the stupendous gorge of the Grand Canyon of the Colorado. More crucial to the whole of North America, however, were the glaciers of the various ice ages that lasted, on and off, for about a million years. The climate of the continent has changed many times. During long periods of arctic temperature, snow piled up until it was thousands of feet thick and the increasing downward pressure turned it into ice. Eventually the pressure became so great that the bottom layers moved outward in all directions. The ice, at times more than a mile thick, spread over millions of square miles, scraped incredible quantities of soil and rock off the land as it passed, hollowed out great channels, and dug holes that became the beds of rivers and lakes.

Where the ice reached its southern limit and began to melt, as in New York State, it left behind great mounds of debris, producing hills such as those along the northern shore of Long Island. At the center of the continent, the melting ice filled a vast basin, known to geologists as Lake Agassiz, which at one time was much larger than the total area of the Great Lakes, and in fact included it. The water from this lake, blocked to the north by the ice sheet itself, was forced to flow southward, thus forming what is now the valley of the Mississippi River. As the ice receded northward, the debris deposited in many places prevented the water from draining away at all, and this is the reason for the many thousands of lakes in Minnesota, Wisconsin, Maine, and Finland.

Another great body of fresh-water lakes, in east central Africa, was mostly formed as a series of catch basins for rain water running down into the Rift, the long valley that lies between the spines of the mountain ranges. Lake Baikal in Siberia, the deepest lake in the world and which contains one-fortieth of all the fresh water in the world, is also caused by a rift in the crust of the earth. Some of the most beautiful lakes in the world, such as Crater Lake in the western United States, are waters that have collected inside the shells of extinct volcanoes. For all their dammed-up splendor, however, the lakes of the world are a very small factor in the world-wide supply of water.

Hydrology

Late in the seventeenth century the English astronomer Halley, who also gave his name to a comet, added up the amount of water from all the rivers that flowed into the Mediterranean. He compared this with the amount of rain and snow that had fallen on the areas drained by these same rivers. The figures came out roughly equal. This first reasoned proof that precipitation fed rivers was the beginning of the science of hydrology, the study of the motion of water upon the land.

Hydrologists, whose basic objective is to increase the amount of water available to mankind, still measure the amount of rain that falls. Around the world this adds up to 80 trillion acre-feet; that is, an acre of water a foot deep annually—an amount that varies from place to place and from year to year. Hydrologists also measure the amount of water that flows to the sea. Still another concern of hydrologists is the amount of ground water—the subterranean reserve that feeds springs and wells, that bubbles up from the bottom of many lakes and streams. Ground water is the reason, uncomprehended by the ancients, why rivers could still flow in the midst of a drought.

It is sometimes wrongly supposed that ground water consists of buried lakes and rivers. These are actually very rare. Most concentrations of ground water are found in such materials as gravel, sand, and limestone; and even in harder rock. Such a concentration, when it can produce a useful amount of water, is known as an *aquifer*. The top of the water-bearing zone, below which the rock or gravel is saturated with moisture, is known as the water table. When a well is dug, the action of a pump to produce a vacuum into which the water is forced upward by pressure from below is ordinarily required to bring a supply to the surface. Where the natural pressure is great enough, the water rises spontaneously to produce an artesian well—so named for the province of Artois in northern France, where the phenomenon was long known to occur. The underground supply that feeds these flowing wells is finally dependent on rainfall, which controls the water table. It is when the water table drops, for example in a dry August, that ordinary wells go dry.

But if you could go deep enough, you would finally strike the water table almost anywhere in the world. Even under the Sahara Desert, where no rain may fall for years at a time, there is a great concentration of water. It is a thousand feet below the surface and is drawn originally from the snowy summits of the Atlas Mountains at the desert's western edge. This supply is believed capable of yielding a flow of 10,000 gallons a second. In Saudi Arabia there is said to be enough ground water to go on flowing, at the rate of a thousand cubic meters a second, for a thousand years before being finally exhausted.

The hydrologist is guided by a number of principles in his search for usable amounts of ground water. Valley floors are obviously more promising than hills, since water is subject to the law of gravity. In dry regions, water-loving plants indicate water at shallow levels. Any area where there are swamps or springs will also have ground water. Rocks are also an important indicator; gravel, sand, limestone, or sandstone at the surface may be a clue to water underneath. Once water is found, the hydrologist, as another service to water users, also analyzes its mineral content and quality.

A basic job in hydrology is to measure the amount of water in a river and the rate at which it flows. This information is needed to determine the capacity required for a dam, the amount available for a hydroelectric plant, the proper height for a flood control project, or the amount that can be taken out for farm, industrial, and human needs. Hydrologists also seek ways of cutting down evaporation for water-storage dams, and economical ways to get rid of water-hungry plants, such as mesquite, that are thieves of ground water. Another hydrological study is to find the best way of preventing the intrusion of salt into freshwater aquifers in coastal areas such as Florida, where a tremendously increasing population is dangerously lowering the water table.

Thus, though the science of hydrology is directly concerned only with fresh water, there is no firm dividing line between it and the study of salt water since all the water sciences are interconnected and refer back finally to the sea.

The sea itself is studied under the very general name of oceanography, a peaceful science with warlike implications that can, if properly applied, do much to save the human race.

2

The Many Sciences of Oceanography

THE fact that the same word "water" in almost all languages describes the substance of the sea as well as lakes and rivers, shows that men have always realized, without benefit of chemical analysis, that basically it was all the same thing. Perhaps they reasoned this way because rain over the sea is just like, and as sweet as, rain on the land. Ancient man may not have realized, however, how dependent he was on the salty seas for his survival. The reason is that the oceans are the major source of the rain that falls. Now man has become increasingly dependent on the sea as a source of food, as a source of minerals, as a highway, and as a dark hiding place for nuclear-powered submarines carrying atomic missiles. He has come to study it as the cause of changes in our weather and as a laboratory to study the geological and geophysical history of our planet. Research into all these manifestations of the sea has greatly increased in recent years. The practical engineering activities going on today have no generally accepted name, but the name usually agreed upon for the glamorous scientific study is oceanography.

The First Oceanographic Studies

The science of oceanography may be said to have begun in 1670, when the English chemist Robert Boyle published his *Observations and Experiments on the Saltness of the Sea.* From talks with ship captains who told him that their ships rode at a different level, with the same load, in different parts of the ocean, Boyle concluded that "saltness" varied with geography, and that some oceans were more buoyant because they were saltier. He was also told how wines were cooled at sea by lowering bottles some distance below the surface and how, if they were lowered too far, the corks would be forced inward. From this and studies of his own, Boyle concluded that water got colder the deeper one went, and that with depth the pressure increased and so did the "saltness."

America's first contribution to oceanography, as to many other fields, was made by Benjamin Franklin. Before he sailed for France as the United States ambassador to the court of Louis XVI, Franklin had already prepared, from information supplied by New England whalers, a map of the Gulf Stream and an account of its warmth and speed. En route to France he concluded that a thermometer could be used for navigation in the current; experimented with using oil to quiet the sea; noted that ships move more easily in deep than in shallow water; invented the sea anchor; explained the phosphorescence of sea water; and developed in theory what amounted to a method of jet propulsion, for moving a ship forward by pumping water rapidly from the stern.

In the last century the most famous American oceanographer was Matthew Maury. As a midshipman, aged twenty, he sailed around the world in the USS *Vincennes.* Later he wrote the first textbook in oceanography, *Physical Geography of the Sea.*

In it he charted the currents of the ocean, showed their stability, and demonstrated their enormous influence on climate. He showed navigators how to work with the sea instead of fighting it. He also recognized the complexity of the sea bottom. "Could the waters of the Atlantic be drawn off," he wrote, "so as to expose to view this great sea-gash, which separates continents, and extends from the Arctic to the Antarctic, it would present a scene most rugged, grand, and imposing. The very ribs of the solid earth, with the foundations of the sea, would be brought to light and we should have presented the empty cradle of the ocean."

Captain Maury founded the Hydrographic Office of the United States Navy and did much to interest the world in the science of the sea. He was a difficult man, however, and aroused a great deal of controversy by venturing upon some sweeping generalizations for which he did not have sufficient evidence. His reputation was damaged, too, by his bitterness over the outcome of the Civil War, after which he exiled himself for many years to England.

Most texts neglect the oceanographic work of two otherwise famous American scientists, Louis Agassiz and his son Alexander. Louis Agassiz, a Swiss, had been interested in all natural science, particularly ichthyology, the study of fishes, and his fame was such that Harvard created a department of biology for him. When a Coast and Geodetic Survey ship, the *Hassler,* was being sent in 1871 around Cape Horn to California, Agassiz was invited along to take samples from the sea. Toward the end of his distinguished career, a wealthy Bostonian, Thayer, presented Agassiz with an island in Buzzards Bay, where he could do research in marine life during the summer.

Agassiz' son Alexander was primarily interested in geology

—the prehistoric Lake Agassiz was named for him—but he did go to England for a number of years to help sort out the collections made from aboard the HMS *Challenger,* the English ship which made the first formal scientific voyage to discover the facts about the sea—probably the most famous of all oceanographic expeditions.

In England during the 1850s and 1860s there was a great increase in curiosity about the sea. A British naturalist, Edward Forbes, published studies of his dredging operations in the Aegean, from which he concluded that there was no life deeper than 1800 feet. The publication in 1844 and 1846 of Charles Darwin's books on the voyage of the *Beagle* showed the possibilities of scientific voyages. The laying of the Atlantic telegraph cable from 1857 to 1866 had shown that the bottom of the sea had many irregularities. A steam engine that was developed for hauling in fishing nets was quickly seen to be adaptable to handling other equipment in deep water.

It was at the initiative of Captain C. Wyville Thompson that the British Navy was induced to provide the *Challenger,* a 2300-ton surplus vessel, for an expedition to find out just what lay below seas of the world. The ship, which used both steam and sail, had all her guns removed and a seagoing laboratory was built, with quarters for six scientists and a staff artist. The ship's officers were selected for their surveying experience and their interest in scientific matters. The ship sailed from Portsmouth, England, in December 1872. After nine stormy days, it made its first station, a stop to take observations, in the Bay of Biscay. A dredge found a depth of 1125 fathoms, or 6750 feet, and brought up enough ice-cold mud from the bottom to chill a bottle of champagne to toast the voyage's success. The mud consisted of globigerina ooze, a sediment made up of tiny globular fossil animals.

Challenger spent three and a half years in circumnavigating the earth, with no purpose other than to satisfy the priceless curiosity of man; oceanography for military and commercial purposes came much later. The ship traveled to Portugal and the Canary Islands; across the Atlantic to St. Thomas, and Nova Scotia; south to Brazil, eastward again to South Africa; then south to the bleak, uninhabited Kerguelen Islands, and even farther south in search of the Antarctic continent. Land was not found, but there was trouble with icebergs and terrible gales, and the voyagers spent "many a fearful and perilous night." Then *Challenger* moved on to Australia, where all hands rested and were entertained for a month. The ship took off again for New Zealand, then headed north to the Fiji Islands, the Philippines, and Japan; it then turned south again to Hawaii, rounded Cape Horn, and proceeded home to England.

One sailor was put ashore in Brazil with yellow fever, another was killed in an accident off Capetown, and a German biologist, the only man aboard with a Ph.D., died of natural causes off the coast of Chile. The ship halted at 362 oceanographic stations,* lost twenty-eight thermometers, and broke her dredging line eleven times. She found one spot in the Pacific 2435 fathoms deep, so far down that it took two and a half hours to let out the lead line and haul it back. Oceanography was hard, hard work.

The *Challenger* expedition had hoped to find out how deep the sea really was, what there was on the bottom, whether sea water was alike in all the oceans, and whether there were any survivors from prehistoric time still living in the great depths.

After traveling 69,000 miles, dredging the bottom, making depth soundings, sampling the water and taking its temperature, the scientists could announce, in a report that filled

* An oceanographic station is a scientific checkup of some particular location in the sea.

twenty volumes and took almost as many years to prepare, that there was life in the sea at every depth; that the bottom of the sea was by no means flat; that there were numerous great currents in the seas; that sea water and its temperature were more or less the same everywhere (though this turned out later to be a little less than exact); that all the chemical elements in the world existed in the sea; and that there were thousands of species of life in the sea still waiting to be classified. Although a vast amount more has been learned about the nature of the sea, nothing has been discovered since the voyage of *Challenger* that very seriously disagrees with her findings.

In the years following the voyage of *Challenger,* interest in marine science grew slowly. The British government usually kept a ship of the same name in commission to do research; the Germans subsidized a series of oceanographic vessels under the name of *Meteor;* and in 1910 the Prince of Monaco, great-grandfather of Rainier III, an enthusiastic amateur, began an oceanographic institute and drew the first map of the bottom of the sea, indicating many of its irregularities. At about the same time a large institution was formed at Naples for the study of marine biology.

Oceanography in the United States was stimulated by Professor W. E. Ritter of the University of California, a zoologist who roamed up and down the coast during the summer studying the animal life of the Pacific. As early as 1903, Dr. Ritter began setting up a field station near San Diego that received the backing of the newspaper publisher E. R. Scripps and his older sister, Miss E. B. Scripps. In 1912 the project was absorbed by the University of California, and in 1925 it became known as the Scripps Institution of Oceanography.

On the East Coast the United States Bureau of Fisheries followed the lead of Louis Agassiz in establishing its own research center for marine biology, at the little town of Woods Hole on Cape Cod. In 1927, Columbus O'Donnell Iselin, a wealthy recent graduate of Harvard, took his yacht and a small group of friends on a quasi-scientific voyage into the Gulf of Maine. Since his father and grandfather had been yachtsmen and Iselin himself had more or less grown up on boats, his interest in science made it almost inevitable that he would take up oceanography. When in 1930 Iselin and his teacher, Professor Henry B. Bigelow of Harvard, decided to set up a formal oceanographic institution, with the aid of grants from the Rockefeller and Carnegie foundations, Woods Hole appeared the logical place for it.

These two centers, one on the Pacific and one on the Atlantic, were all that existed in the "scientific community" of oceanography in the United States until after the end of World War II.

A Definition of Oceanography

Oceanography consists basically of measuring things in the sea and assigning them some sort of number on a scale, then interpreting the results and fitting these into already known basic laws of physics and biology or, if necessary, synthesizing new laws for them. Observations such as the temperature of the water, and its saltiness; the depth from the surface to the bottom; the amount of oxygen; the number of different animal and plant species; the speed and direction, and the depth and volume, of an ocean current; and the heights of waves can all be measured and assigned figures. In most cases the measuring can be done by technicians, not requiring the skills of true oceanographers.

Oceanographers used to be described as "sailors who use long words." Their science was "anything that has to be studied from a ship." What with instruments such as satellites, computers, submersibles, and moored buoys, oceanographers now can do many things that do not require their presence on the deck of a vessel, but the elite among them are still those who go to sea. When two young scientists, both with Ph.D. degrees, were interviewed about the theoretical work they were doing with ocean currents in an office at Woods Hole, one of them asked, "Have you met any *real* oceanographers yet?"

An oceanographer today has to study all the basic sciences—physics, chemistry, biology, geology, and meteorology—as they relate to the sea. Any *real* oceanographer is also something of a sailor, or at least knows the language of sailing. Although in practice all ocean scientists specialize, they must know a good deal about all the related subjects because all studies of the sea must be like the sea itself, three-dimensional.

Ocean Currents

Ocean currents are like vast rivers, without any stream beds to guide them, that run through the comparatively motionless seas around them, rivers that make the Amazon seem a creek. Many forces affect their behavior. Water at the surface in the tropics is quite warm, and at the poles it is very cold. Warm water expands and becomes lighter; colder water—up until the point of freezing, when it starts to expand—becomes dense and heavy. As the cold polar water sinks, the warm water from the Equator flows out to take its place. Thus, polar water moves along the bottom toward the tropics, while tropical water moves north and south in the direction of the poles.

The process is speeded up by the prevailing winds on either side of the Equator, which regularly blow toward the west because of the earth's eternal rotation. The warm surface water near the Equator is therefore pushed generally westward by these winds. When these currents are blocked by the presence of continents, they have to move somewhere. In the northern hemisphere they turn toward the right and in the southern hemisphere they turn toward the left—a phenomenon known as the Coriolis effect.

Currents in the Pacific are less obvious than those in the Atlantic because the Pacific is so much larger. The north equatorial current of the Pacific flows west until it strikes the Philippines. Then it is driven north, past Japan, where it has the name, among others, of the Kuroshio Current. It splits around Japan, one stream going north to the Arctic, the other flowing toward North America, where it runs south down the coast toward the Equator and is known as the California Current. The course is similar in the southern Pacific, though it has been less well charted.

In the southern Atlantic the equatorial current, after it strikes South America, is known as the Brazil Current. It flows down toward the South Pole, to meet the Antarctic Current—in a much studied phenomenon called the Convergence—and, as the Benguela Current, flows northward again up the African coast.

The equivalent of the Kuroshio Current in the North Atlantic is the Gulf Stream. Because it flows across the route of so much sea traffic, it has been more extensively studied than any other ocean river.

The Gulf Stream

Benjamin Franklin thought a map could be drawn to show the exact position of the Gulf Stream. Oceanographers have since discovered, however, that after it has passed Cape Hatteras it meanders and even loops around itself. Its position may change by as much as a hundred miles to the east or west. The Gulf Stream is now regarded as beginning where the Florida Current meets the north-flowing waters of the equatorial current, near the Bahamas, in a fairly shallow part of the sea known as the Blake Plateau. As it flows north, the sea level of the Gulf Stream rises. When it reaches Hatteras its volume has increased ten times over, to carry 150 million tons of water a second. Farther on—exactly where or when is still not known—the Gulf Stream finally breaks up and disperses.

A part of the water circles southward to enter the Sargasso Sea, fabled for its seaweed calm. Another part flows north to meet the cold Labrador Current, which travels southward to the Grand Banks of Newfoundland, known for their fogs and excellent fishing. Under the influence of the westerly winds and because the curve of the coast is to the east, the Stream aims in the general direction of Europe but does not actually reach it. Winds blowing over it, however, are sufficiently warmed that the climate of Ireland, England, and Scandinavia is tempered by them. The remaining waters of the Stream itself turn south again to be warmed once more at the Equator.

Although this much is known, a number of problems remain. An English oceanographer, J. C. Swallow, reasoned that to dispose of the masses of water moving north, there must be a deep countercurrent bringing some of the volume south. In 1958, during the International Geophysical Year, the British ship *Discovery,* working with the Woods Hole ship *Atlantis,* took measurements, using a neutrally buoyant float that Swallow had invented, and found just such a deep flow.

The cause of the meanderings of course, and ways of predicting them accurately, are still being studied. It seems likely that they are influenced by the topography of the ocean floor; but this is by no means certain, since it is not even known just how deep the Gulf Stream actually is.

The idea of the Gulf Stream as a simple "river in the

ocean" does not do justice to a very complicated phenomenon. It is continually being studied from Woods Hole, even in the roughest weather, both because of the influence of its movements upon the weather of North America and because of its importance to the fishing industry, as well as to commercial shipping. The Marine Biological Laboratory has an oceanographic seaplane equipped with a radiation thermometer which can find the warm edge of the Gulf Stream and thus detect its changes of course. The plane also seeks schools of fish, studies the changing shoreline of Cape Cod and the motion of dunes, and watches out for icebergs; and every other summer it locates the Stream for the benefit of sailors in the yacht race from Newport to Bermuda.

The currents inshore from the Gulf Stream are also being studied at Woods Hole. One scientist has been doing this for ten years by means of drift bottles, in a process sometimes called "mail order oceanography." His main assistance has come from twelve United States lightships, which have been dropping bottles into the sea for a decade. So far 30,000 bottles have been set adrift and cards have been mailed back by the finders of 10 per cent of these. Certain findings based on these returns have now been published. One is proof that rivers like the Hudson, as would be expected, have a great influence on currents offshore. In drought periods the flow of rivers is greatly decreased, so that the usual inshore current to the south reverses itself and runs north. (A complaint about drift bottle research is that "there is a birth notice and an obituary, but no biography." There is no way of telling what happened in between.)

The Cromwell Current

Research on ocean currents in the Pacific historically centered on the Kuroshio, or Black Current so essential to Japan. In 1956, however, a young oceanographer, Townsend

Cromwell, who was working for the United States Bureau of Commercial Fisheries, found that near the Equator the water 100 to 200 feet down was moving rapidly to the east. This was surprising, since the water on the surface at the Equator always moves west at a considerable speed, and since it had been taken for granted that the waters underneath moved in the same direction. The Cromwell Current, as it is now called, never moves off the Equator more than two degrees, a distance of 120 miles. Later investigation by oceanographers at the Scripps Institution showed that it carries 40 million tons of water a second, as much as the Gulf Stream at the Bahamas. It is a broad ribbon of water more than 200 miles wide and a few hundred feet thick, and all the water around it flows in the opposite direction.

Cromwell's discovery created something of a sensation. Was there a similar stream in the Atlantic? Investigation showed that there was, after Allyn Vine of Woods Hole thought of an economical way to check the matter. In 1961 he persuaded the Chief of Naval Operations to send a message to a nuclear submarine on its way back from the South Atlantic. The submarine was ordered, on reaching a point near the Equator, to assume a 45° angle at a depth of 300 feet and to steer due north for five minutes. The submarine captain, though puzzled by this strange order, went ahead—and found it impossible to carry out. The position of the submarine was such that the pressures of the great Cromwell Current and the countercurrent above it were exactly equal, and the vessel was forced to remain stationary. Thus far, attempts to find the same phenomenon in the Indian Ocean have been unsuccessful except for one month in the year.

That the current remains at the Equator is evidence that it is somehow caused by the rotation of the earth. Waters off the center are deflected by the spin of the ocean floor beneath them—in other words, by the Coriolis effect, which drives waters north of the Equator to the right and waters south of it to the left. The force reaches its maximum at each of the poles, but since at the Equator there is no spin, the Coriolis effect there is zero. Unfortunately, the young discoverer of this equatorial river was killed in a flying accident in Mexico on his way to join another expedition.

Air-Sea Interaction

The behavior of currents is only one concern of oceanographers. At New York University and many other institutions, scientists pursue the understanding of wave action. They are particularly interested in the interaction at the boundary between air and sea, where waves are formed, and where the turbulence caused by the energy of the sun leads to evaporation at the surface. One of these scientists said, "We don't really know how turbulence here really works. We have no way yet of accurately measuring the amount of evaporation or the *rate* of the exchange of energy. We need to find out *how* turbulence carries away heat from the ocean." Since this process is intimately bound up with the hydrologic cycle, it is believed that once the question of turbulence is solved, an accurate ten-day weather forecast may be possible. By then a much better information network will no doubt have been established around the world, partially by a wider use of satellites than at present.

Waves and Sea Level

A Navy-sponsored project New York University is working on is a system of wave prediction for the North Atlantic. The original research was based on a knowledge of the sea-level wind speed and direction at some 500 different points on the ocean, at one particular moment. With a computer, the scientists then "hindcast" the waves from historical data. From this picture of the behavior of the winds at a particular time, plus wind forecasts for short intervals in the future, it will soon be possible to predict wave conditions for the next twelve, twenty-four, and thirty-six hours. To keep the system going, it will be necessary to have new information every six hours from each of the 500 points. Clearly the information would be invaluable to a wartime fleet, an aircraft carrier, or a task force about to make a landing. Already, a graduate thesis on this subject has enabled the Navy to save a million dollars a year by showing how to predict and avoid heavy seas. The fastest way to cross the ocean is no longer the Great Circle route, but a course where the ship will meet the least resistance from waves.

The Lamont Geological Observatory at Columbia University is concerned, among many other things, with "internal waves." These may occur at great depths, often in mid-ocean, and have no obvious relation to the waves on the surface. What produces them is still unknown, but they may be related to the point of contact between fresh and salt water.

What was once called "sea level," it is now realized, is an inaccurate way of referring to the sea's changing and distorted surface. Tides, influenced by the ocean bottom, may change sea level by many feet. The atmosphere affects the level by its varying pressure. Sea level at the mouth of a large river is always higher than elsewhere. The level of the sea along rainy shores is likewise higher than in mid-ocean. Sea level in such waters as the Baltic is much lower in winter, when freezing slows down and may even stop the rivers that feed them. The monsoons in the Indian Ocean raise the sea level, as do storms in shallow seas. Finally, the heating and cooling of the earth cause the sea to expand and contract.

Sounds in the Sea

About thirty years ago it was realized that the saltiness, pressure, and temperature of the sea all affect the speed at which sound travels through water: an increase in any of the three increases the rate of speed. Interest in the subject then grew intense because of its bearing on undersea warfare. The speed of sound in the sea is five times faster than in any other medium, and it can be transmitted directionally with great precision. Listening gear in the sea can detect sounds from great distances, though locating the source is complicated by the three variables mentioned above, as well as by the existence of thermoclines—sharp gradients between warm and cold water. In 1935 the invention of an instrument called the bathythermograph enabled researchers to keep constant track of the ocean temperature at various depths, and to spot thermoclines. The bathythermograph was carried by many vessels of the United States Navy during World War II.

The applications of the behavior of sound in the ocean are not only military. The rugged features of the ocean bottom have been discovered by the use of electrically operated sounding gear which send out a "pinging" impulse. The echo of the impulse is timed, and, since the approximate speed of sound through water is known, to find the distance the sound has traveled is a matter of calculating the difference between impulse and return. Fortunately, the calculation is done automatically.

The device has many uses in navigation. Until scientists understood how to use sound in their investigations, man's concern with the ocean bottom, for practical purposes, had to end as soon as he got into water deeper than the keel of his ship. Now sound can be used even for navigation in such well-known areas as the deep ocean canyon of the Hudson River.

A fairly recent development is the Precision Graphic Recorder, an automatic sounding device that marks the depth under the ship as it travels. The continual records of the depth and of the ship's position at the time are correlated with thousands of others, so that eventually an accurate topographic map of the whole ocean bottom will be possible.

These instruments, however, record only the distance to the upper level of the sediments on the ocean floor. These may be hundreds of feet thick, and thus the records based on sounding devices do not reveal the nature of the solid crust of the earth itself. A geophysicist, Dr. Maurice Ewing, has developed a technique known as seismic shooting in order to study the structures concealed by the sediments. The technique consists of dropping depth charges and timing the return of the sound from the bottom. The sound first bounces off the sediment and then, more slowly, off the true bottom. The return is monitored from a second ship that may be as much as fifty miles away. The quality of the returning sound also gives an indication of the kind of rock that reflected it. Dropping depth charges off the stern of a ship, sometimes at thirty-second intervals, is tedious and even dangerous work; at least one man has lost his life in handling the high explosives. Other methods of finding the true ocean floor have therefore been developed, but depth charges still give the greatest accuracy.

Another method of studying the earth itself is the deep-sea seismograph, modeled after the device used to register earthquakes but modified to withstand corrosion and the pressures of the deep sea. The United States Navy financed it as a possible means of differentiating between earthquakes and atomic explosions. It provides scientists with a way of listening, in inaccessible places, to the sounds made by the earth's unstable crust, in which an average of three recordable quakes take place every hour of every day the year round.

One deep-sea seismograph was tested in 15,000 feet of water off Bermuda, where it could execute fifteen different commands on signal by remote control. The instrument was so delicate that it also recorded the noise of waves breaking on distant shores.

The Bottom of the Ocean

The picture of the ocean bottom produced by means of sound is far from complete today. Only two per cent of the earth under the sea has been charted with the accuracy required of a land map, and there are many millions of square miles for which no soundings have been taken at all. Nevertheless, the vague idea many people have that the bottom of the sea is just a wide sandy plain has proved to be quite false. There are some abyssal plains, but there are also mountain ranges longer than any found on land, deep trenches along the edges of continents, isolated mountain peaks—also known as sea-mounts—canyons through parts of the continental shelf that seem to have been carved by great rivers (as well as canyons unrelated to any existing river mouths), and rifts that suggest that some of the mountain ridges may be splitting apart.

Ever since *Challenger* found a depth in the Pacific of more than 14,000 feet, oceanographers have been looking for still deeper spots. At one time a trench near the Kurile Islands off Japan was the deepest known; then one off Mindanao in the Philippines set a new record, followed by another off Tonga in the South Pacific. Then scientists aboard the British ship *Discovery* found a trench off the Marianas southeast of Guam. It was calculated, and later confirmed by a ship from the Scripps Institution, that the deepest part of the Marianas Trench is 35,810 feet down, a mile deeper than Mount Everest is high. As of 1967 this was still the record figure.

In the Atlantic the greatest depth found so far is a trench north of Puerto Rico. In 1964 it was investigated by the Lamont Geological Observatory, along with the French Navy's submersible vessel, *Archimede.* The expedition turned out to be quite frustrating. *Archimede* was impractical as a research tool. It could not maneuver, it could not bring up samples of the bottom, and it was difficult to control. The Lamont vessel, *Conrad,* did some deep-water dredging on its own, however—and came up with samples of rock that contradicted each other. The work of the expedition is still being evaluated. Meanwhile, the origin of the Puerto Rico Trench and others like it has not yet been explained.

The Mid-Atlantic Ridge

A major contribution by the Lamont Geological Observatory was the discovery of a rift in the Mid-Atlantic Ridge. This tremendous range of peaks beneath the sea begins in the far North Atlantic and runs more or less along the center of the ocean into the South Atlantic. Here, to the south of Africa, part of the ridge meets a similar range that extends into the Indian Ocean. The Mid-Atlantic Ridge breaks the surface of the sea to form Iceland and the Azores, where the perfect cone of Mount Pico, 10,000 feet high, is actually the summit of a 27,000-foot mountain if measured from its base on the ocean floor. These are regions of continuous volcanic activity. As recently as November 1963, the new volcanic island of Surtsey rose off the coast of Iceland, and several new volcanoes have appeared with a few miles of Mount Pico.

At Lamont Observatory the story of the rift in the ridge begins in the geophysics department, where Marie Tharp had begun to draw a chart of the floor of the North Atlantic. Of the few available soundings the greatest number had been made in the 1920s by the German ship *Meteor,* and the records had been destroyed during the bombing of Berlin. Miss Tharp did have enough soundings, however, to suggest that there might be a valley running down the middle of the already known mountain range. Bruce Heezen, an oceanographer, agreed that such a thing was possible, but added that there was hardly enough information to give cause for excitement.

So the idea lay dormant for some time, until the Bell Telephone Company asked Heezen for information that might explain a series of breaks in the transatlantic telephone cable. The answer was clearly earthquakes. When Miss Tharp noticed that the breaks all occurred in her hypothetical valley, Heezen took the matter up with Maurice Ewing, who found it plausible. When, wondering how far the rift might extend, the researchers checked the findings available for the ridge in the South Atlantic, they discovered what appeared to be an extension of the same rift. An investigation of the high Carlsberg Ridge in the Indian Ocean and the Albatross Plateau in the Pacific off Mexico showed similar valleys.

In the cautious way of scientists, five years of study and investigation went by before the appearance of a paper signed by Tharp, Heezen, and Ewing, describing a geological phenomenon that ran around the globe. Atomic submarines had confirmed the existence of the rifts in the mountains under the North Pole; the San Andreas Fault in California and the Rift Valley of Africa seemed to conform to the same pattern. The recently discovered East Pacific Rise is apparently part of the same system which turns out to be a 40,000-mile chain of undersea ridges with a rift down its center, running almost twice around the earth.

This bulge in the crust of the earth differs in many ways from the rest of the ocean bottom. It is thinner than the earth's crust elsewhere, and it is an area of frequent earthquakes and of a high rate of heat flow from the interior. The implications are that the crust of the earth is slowly breaking apart at the seams, and that earthquakes in such areas are part of the process. The earth evidently is expanding gradually as the result of heat forces from within. Scientists say that the rocks of the earth's mantle, down to the molten core 1600 miles deep, are slowly bubbling up and turning over like oatmeal cooking in a pot. Such activity would explain why none of the sediments found in the central oceans have been more than a million years old—which, geologically speaking, is still young.

Underneath the Bottom of the Sea

Over the last few years, oceanographic research has become increasingly complex and expensive. It has become clear that cooperative programs among the private oceanographic institutions would solve many problems. Thus in 1964 Scripps, Woods Hole, Lamont, and the University of Miami signed an agreement to cooperate in deep-sea drilling. The agreement set up an organization called the Joint Oceanographic Institutions Deep Earth Sampling, known for simplicity as JOIDES. The four groups agreed on twenty areas in both the Pacific and the Atlantic where deep-sea drilling might be profitable.

Upon learning that a drilling vessel, *Caldrill,* chartered by the Pan American Oil Company, was due to sail from California to Halifax, Nova Scotia, in the spring of 1965, the group arranged to employ it during its journey along the coast of Florida. The drilling went on for thirty days at six spots in the area of the Blake Plateau, a geological riddle in that it seems to have no counterpart anywhere else on earth. It is deeper than the Continental Shelf, but much shallower than the deep sea. It is unlike any island formation. Its geological age is different from that of the shelf. How did it come to be there?

Under the direction of a scientist from Lamont, the drilling began in fairly shallow water, twenty-two miles from Jacksonville, and then finally moved 250 miles offshore, to where the depth is 3500 feet and the outer edge of the plateau slopes down a steep cliff to the deep sea. The deepest hole drilled was 1050 feet below the ocean bottom, so far a record for scientific purposes.

Among the results was the discovery at the twenty-two-mile location of two freshwater aquifers where artesian water gushed thirty feet into the air. This added greatly to the known water resources of Florida. The drilling indicated the presence on the shelf of economically important phosphorite beds. Numerous fossils discovered in the drill cores will be of great value in determining the geologic history of the area. Very little sediment from the recent Tertiary age was found on the plateau, although it was abundant closer to shore—a fact suggesting that the plateau is geologically a very new development. Further study of the cores should produce many interesting findings. The sponsors of the project now believe that scientific drilling is possible in water as deep as 6000 feet.

The Mohole

Another project, the Mohole, calls for drilling in even deeper water. The idea, although terribly difficult to carry out, is itself very simple. It is merely to dig far deeper into the earth than anyone has ever dug before, to find out what is there. It was first proposed by men from the University of California and Princeton University. An international congress of scientists that took place in Toronto in 1957 approved the idea.

The Mohole is named for Andrija Mohorovicic, a Yugoslav seismologist noted for his measurements of the shock waves from earthquakes. He decided that, because the speed of the earthquake sound varied, the earth must be composed of two distinct layers of rock. The sound traveled faster through the interior layer known as the mantle than through the less dense outer crust. The boundary or discontinuity between the two was given the nickname of "the Moho."

One object of the Mohole is to discover what the earth's mantle is made of. Cores brought up during the digging should tell much about the history of climate, about the nature of early life, and about the origin of the oceans, the continents, and the earth itself. Digging through the boundary between the crust and the mantle may also tell how old the earth is; whether it is getting hotter or colder; whether the world's land areas started as one continent or as five or six; whether the inside is solid, gas, or liquid; and whether the North and South Poles have shifted since the beginning. With all this new knowledge, it may even be possible to predict earthquakes in advance.

The Mohole project, unfortunately, has run into considerable economic and political difficulty and, in spite of the enormous scientific dividends it might produce, it is a moot question if and when it will ever be carried out.

Micropaleontology

The theory that the continents have shifted over the ages receives support from the science of micropaleontology, the study of fossil sea shells too small to be recognized without a strong magnifying glass. Some of them must be studied under an electron microscope. They are particularly useful in geological studies because great numbers can be brought to the surface unbroken in sedimentary cores. Microfossils, which have been used for some time, too, by oil geologists, provide much information about changes in climate and in the earth's surface.

The known habits of their living relatives tell a great deal about the conditions under which the fossil remains once lived. Many species of diatoms, for instance, live only in fresh water, and all radiolarians live only in salt water. Conodonts are particularly useful to oil geologists because they are known to have become extinct in the Triassic period, 240 million years ago, when oil deposits are believed to have been laid down. Discoasters, which died out abruptly about a million years ago, are interesting because they may be a clue to the beginning of the first ice age, at least in the Antarctic, as well as to the beginning of the Pleistocene era with its rigorous climate.

The most abundant of these fossils are the foraminifera, single-celled animals that over the last 500 million years have envolved rapidly into thousands of different species, leaving their shells in the form of sediment at the bottom of the sea. A great number of different forms have left an excellent record of the conditions in which they grew. Since in cold water the shells of foraminifera coil to the left, whereas in warm water they coil to the right, their fossils are a clue to the changing climate. Fossils from cores found in the North Atlantic, and dated radioactively to 11,000 years ago, change quite abruptly from left-coiling to right-coiling—a discovery suggesting that the ice age ended at that date rather than 20,000 years ago, as had previously been supposed.

Studies of microfossils in the Atlantic floor sediments have produced none that are more than 100 million years old. Since microfossil sediments much older than this have been found in rock that is now above sea level, it is presumed that tremendous changes took place about that time which wiped out all the previous history and gave the Atlantic its present form.

The Changing Magnetism of the Earth

That the earth itself is a magnet has been known for many hundreds of years. The Arabs discovered almost a thousand years ago that a magnetized iron needle, a compass, will point more or less accurately north and south in response to the attraction of the magnetic Poles. A recently developed tool, the magnetometer, seems to show that the Poles have moved over many millions of years, and that now the magnetism of numerous points on the crust of the earth has altered.

The substance of the earth has no magnetism in a molten state, but the lines of magnetism within this material develop as it cools. The lines conform to the direction of the magnetic field from the Poles at the time, so as to be permanently fixed in position. If such hardened material is later moved out of position by some kind of earth force, the lines will still conform to the position in which they hardened.

Scientists at the Scripps Oceanographic Institution in California have now discovered that the crust of the earth underneath parts of the Pacific has moved as much as 700 miles. In 1959 one of their vessels towed a magnetometer all the way from Samoa to San Diego. The map drawn from this and later experiments concerning the earth's magnetic field showed long narrow lines that did not match other lines nearby. It was as though a set of parallel railroad tracks had been violently separated so that the points which should join were moved far apart. The dislocated lines could be made to match, however, if a map of the Pacific was cut along a fault zone and put together. Now the railroad tracks, or magnetic lines, would match perfectly, indicating that the crusts had once fitted together before the fault occurred.

It is not known why such faults occur in the earth's crust. One theory is that the tides of water that sweep over it every day cause fatigue in weak areas, so that the crust finally yields to pressures stronger than those which keep it in place. A complete magnetic map of the world should some day explain the earth's structural history.

Oceanographic Instruments

Because the ocean is opaque—you can't see through it—as well as so deep that it is still not easy to go down into it, instruments are vitally necessary to replace and extend the senses man uses in his natural environment. The invention and development of such instruments goes on at all research institutions. Initially, of course, there has to be either a ship or some kind of platform to carry the men and the instruments. *Challenger,* the earliest such vessel, carried a lead line to measure depth, a dredge and coring tube to bring up samples from the bottom, nets for catching deep-sea creatures, a thermometer, and a bottle to bring up salt water for analysis, but not a great deal else.

Since that time, the variety of instruments has proliferated almost beyond reckoning. One of the more important is the Nansen bottle, an invention of the Norwegian explorer of that name, which is lowered to a certain depth, then mechanically tripped so that water samples from that level can be sealed in. A thermometer attached to the bottle records the temperature at the moment the sample is secured. In the ship's laboratory the water is analyzed for its salt content, its proportion of oxygen, and any other chemical information that may be desired. Also essential is the plankton tow net, a bag made of very fine mesh used to capture those microscopic forms of sea life that float rather than propel themselves.

Among other recent developments are radio buoys to measure currents, radar buoys with submerged drogues for the same purpose, oceanographic winches for deep-sea samples, numerous special cameras for deep-sea photography, thermometers that will withstand great heat and pressure, various kinds of automatic depth recorders, and gravimeters for measuring the relative gravity of a portion of the earth.

All these ingenious devices, unfortunately, are subject to the fact that sea water is one of the most corrosive liquids known to man. There is a high mortality among instruments. Less of a problem, though real enough not to be very funny, is that sharks have no discrimination and will bite at anything in the water, not excepting heavy steel cables. Although little can be done about sharks, a large-scale program is going on to find materials resistant to sea corrosion.

A new kind of oceanographic technology, however, may be able simply to ignore such hazards. Satellites are now being studied by oceanographers for their possibilities in research. Mariners have already been using them for some time for very accurate navigation. The vehicles put up by the nation's space agency were among the subjects considered by scientists at a conference in 1965 on oceanography in space. Among the ideas put forth at the meeting were that forest fires could be detected by infrared sensors on satellites, and that extensive water pollution could be detected in the same way. Geothermal resources, such as Old Faithful and the geysers of New Zealand, might also be found in this manner, as could radioactive deposits of ore. Satellites could be used to measure the heat budget of the sun, the surface temperature of the sea and the true sea level as distinct from the mean local level, and to study regular tides and the oceanwide swells caused by earthquakes. They might also help determine the slope of the surface of the sea and give long-range wave and weather forecasts to aid in routing ships. Fisheries would be greatly assisted by satellites that could trace currents and upwellings of cold water, study fish schools and submarine movements by detecting bioluminescence (popularly known as phosphorescence); and monitor the "red tides" that cause enormous fish kills in the Caribbean.

On the other hand, satellites cannot be of much use very far beneath the surface of the sea. To measure the characteristics of sound under water below the noise and interference of surface waves, the United States Navy and the Scripps Institution have developed a radical new instrument called FLIP, for Floating Instrument Platform. It consists of a 355-foot ship without any means of propelling itself. Once it has been towed to its destination, however, it can flip into a vertical position so that 300 feet of its length go straight down into the sea while the remaining 55 feet stand straight up in the air. FLIP is as stable as a fence post, and in a storm that mounted 35-foot waves it moved less than three inches. The work FLIP does is also possible for submarines, but seventy-five such platforms can be built for the cost of one modern submarine.

The Navy has also had a part in developing a new type of submersible vessel, conceived by Allyn Vine of the Woods Hole Laboratory and known as *Alvin*. This is a small submarine that holds two men and is useful in all sorts of oceanographic work at depths as great as 6000 feet. To quote the supervisor of the *Alvin* program;

> For many years geologists have had to content themselves with views and samples of the floor of the ocean taken by underwater cameras, by coring equipment or by dredges. Now for the first time these scientists will be able to go to depths of 6000 feet in the ocean, there to view for themselves rock structures, sediment

formations and other areas in the oceanic environment. Biologists, who up to now have relied on trawls and dredges to bring up specimens of deep water marine life, may now go to the deep water and selectively catch the particular species they need.

In addition, *Alvin* will be used to study what are known as the deep scattering layers many hundreds of feet below the surface. So called because they scatter sound signals, the layers are thought to be caused by plankton, although photographs and trawling have not produced evidence to back up the idea. *Alvin,* which can be maneuvered right into such layers, may be able to explain the phenomenon.

With its ability to hover and to maintain neutral buoyancy, *Alvin* should be able to make many contributions to marine biology, and most particularly the social behavior of schools of fish. Such schools, which may number many thousands of a particular species, maneuver in perfect unison, sometimes in very murky water, by some sort of signal that is not at all understood at present. Perhaps a vessel such as *Alvin,* since it can stay motionless in one position for a matter of some hours, may permit observations of fish without frightening them and indicate how messages are transmitted among them. Other problems which *Alvin* may help solve about fish are their migratory and reproductive patterns, their tastes in food, and the nature of their sensory perceptions.

In 1966, even before *Alvin* had begun to be seriously engaged in the research projects for which it was designed, the little submarine was diverted to help solve a most bizarre problem. Early in the year a United States B-52 bomber, which was carrying four hydrogen bombs, collided at 30,000 feet over the southeast coast of Spain with a flying tanker from which it was refueling. When the planes crashed, the bombs were set free to parachute down. Three fell on land and were rescued, after causing considerable concern in the small village nearby; but the fourth bomb went down in the sea. *Alvin* and *Aluminaut,* another research submarine, were flown from the United States to help find it and, after a week or more of search, *Alvin,* working with ocean-going minesweepers of the Sixth Fleet, did just that in more than 2000 feet of water. Efforts to bring the object to the surface were frustrated by murky seas, the swift currents and the bomb's position on a steep ledge that dropped down to a ravine more than 4000 feet deep. *Alvin* succeeded in tying several lines to it, but these broke when the surface vessel tried to haul it up. Finally, a new United States Navy device known as *Curv,* a robot-directed vehicle equipped with a TV camera and controlled by a mother ship, did succeed in attaching two claws to the bomb, and a line was hooked to these. Hauling to the surface was complicated by the fact that *Alvin,* which was standing by, and *Curv* became fouled in the bomb's parachute rigging. After several near disasters, in an atmosphere made all the more tense by an awareness of dealing with an explosive many times more powerful than the one that devastated Hiroshima, the crews finally brought the bomb to the surface. During the two months that it took to make the recovery, *Alvin* made a total of 145 dives.

Marine Biology

From the beginning, oceanographers have been concerned with living things in the sea. *Challenger's* scientists found many strange and exotic specimens. Their major interest was in classifying these into the proper orders and suborders. They knew too little about deep-sea life as a whole, however, to add much to the understanding of why fish are abundant in some places and scarce in others, or why particular fish are restricted to certain habitats; thus they did not learn anything to aid commercial fishing. Today it is realized that a study of plankton, the microscopic food of everything else that lives in the sea, is essential to the problem of supplying protein to the billions of people in the world who are underfed. Plankton studies today concentrate on their geographical distribution—the question of why one species thrives in a particular ocean but not in another—since the presence or absence of plankton determines the supply of fish.

Recent studies have revealed an important but previously unsuspected link in the food chain of marine life. Just as on land, the life cycle in the sea needs sunlight for the process of photosynthesis, upon which the production of all food ultimately depends. In the sea the green plants are known as phytoplankton. These plants are grazed by tiny animals which float or swim only a little and are known as zooplankton. While plankton of all sorts are fed on directly by whales and shellfish, zooplankton are the diet only of carnivorous fish. Little carnivorous fish are eaten by bigger ones. Whenever death occurs, the once living matter decomposes and releases the phosphorus, nitrogen, and carbon needed to repeat the process of photosynthesis. Much of this matter, however, sinks to the sea bottom. Below the 300-foot level there is no longer enough sunlight for green plants to grow; thus it was thought that the decomposed matter was not recovered except as the upwelling caused by deep currents brought it from the bottom.

But now nightmarish monsters have been photographed at tremendous depths, and a shrimp was seen from the bathyscaphe *Trieste* almost seven miles below the surface. Clearly these animals have to eat something. When it was shown in the experiments at Yale that the microscopic zooplankton are capable of assimilating inorganic material, the mystery of the abundance of fish life, in depths where there could be no photosynthesis, had been solved—though it never was a mystery to the fish.

Another current study is of things in the sea that can turn themselves on and off.

Many forms of marine life have the same ability as the firefly to convert chemical energy into light. Among these are certain sponges, jellyfishes, crustaceans, snails, and fishes, and many kinds of plants. (There are, however, no bioluminescent amphibians, reptiles, birds, or mammals.) Scientists at Woods Hole have observed displays of luminescence as strong as moonlight and have counted as many as a hundred flashes a minute. Evidently the phenomenon is important in the lives of many inhabitants of the sea. It may play a part in migration, speed, or swimming direction. It may be used by organisms to recognize their own species, attract prey or repel enemies, or as a sort of headlight for finding their way.

The bathyphotometer, a very sensitive instrument for measuring light, has been used in observing luminescent flashes at ocean depths of more than two miles. A jellyfish left its own portrait in an automatic luminescence camera, at 3000 feet.

Bioluminescence is a mechanism available to about a third of the major divisions of the animal kingdom. Just as the observation of birds helped man learn how to fly, so may the observation of this naturally-produced light teach man much of great importance.

Fishing Research

Considerable effort now goes into finding new kinds of edible fish and new fishing grounds. One discovery has been the phenomenal richness of the waters of the Gulf of Guinea, off the coast of Africa. A ship from the University of Miami that had a part in the discovery was also responsible, in waters nearer home, for bringing to light an entirely new species of fish. Solid black, about an inch long, with a broad, flat head and enormous eyes, it was given the name siphonophore. To find a new family of fishes today is an extraordinary achievement, particularly in the surface waters of the western Atlantic, where so much scientific work has gone on for so long. The discovery illustrates the degree to which the oceans still remain untapped and unexplored.

At Miami, studies are also in progress of how pink shrimp, which spawn in the Dry Tortugas, make their way as larvae to the Everglades, which they use as a nursery. What scientists are looking for is some yet unknown bottom current that would sweep the helpless eggs along. Shrimp are the most valuable fishery product in the United States and the demand is so great that 100 million pounds are imported every year. Scientific studies may help to increase the production at home.

Another Miami project has used a boat and a light airplane to study the process by which sharks are able to close in on their quarry. They can spot prey from as much as 200 yards away, even though they can't see it from that distance. Apparently sharks hear vibrations in the water which alert them, whereupon they approach with great speed and accuracy. The presence of a struggling fish or a threshing swimmer evidently generates sound waves that constitute a dinner bell for a cruising shark.

On the west coast of the United States a great deal of work has gone on in the case of the vanishing sardines. In the 1930s a yearly harvest of about 700,000 tons of sardines off the coast of California constituted the industry celebrated in John Steinbeck's *Cannery Row*. Today only a few tons a year are being brought in. To the question of why they disappeared, one suggested answer is that they were starved out as a result of a change in the sea's nutrient character. Another is that they were overfished and that the anchovies, of which there is now an enormous population in the area, simply took over.

Another area of interest is that of marine plants which may be used by man. The Japanese already use seaweed for food, and in California it is harvested for fertilizer and for use as a fixative in ice cream. Primitive man used seaweed to cure goiter and constipation and as an antibiotic. Research is now being conducted on other medical uses for marine plants and animals, including poisonous species that might serve the same beneficial purposes as strychnine, atropine, arsenic and other lethal substances.

In Hawaii a trained porpoise named Keiki (Hawaiian for "child"), a captive since infancy, was released for the first time in his adult life into the open sea. He returned upon hearing an underwater sound signal—possibly because he feared the unknown environment and was dependent on the researchers both emotionally and as food sources. In the open ocean he ignored the numerous fish that were available. During Keiki's training in a tank, someone swam with him for an hour every day, so that he quickly became very tame and affectionate. The question now is whether Keiki would be able to survive in a school of untamed porpoises. They are highly social animals, with a long period of dependency of the young, and no one knows what would happen if a stranger tried to join the group. If one could, it might be possible thus to observe and understand much of porpoise behavior.

There are countless research projects in the many sciences of oceanography. For the future, there are many large questions for which answers are still needed. For instance, is it true, as suggested by the faults around the edge of the Pacific, that the whole ocean basin is rotating counterclockwise?

Another question which oceanography may help solve is whether the crusts under the continents are permanent or only a phase in geological time. The science is also deeply concerned with the history of the water in the sea and whether or not ocean currents have always moved in the same way they do today.

Of biological interest is the question of how deep forms of life manage to exist in such very high pressures and at temperatures just a few degrees above freezing. There is curiosity about how the "living fossils" found recently in the sea managed to survive and about the differing rates of evolutionary change among species.

In terms of sea water, scientists face such questions as how temperature walls (thermoclines) develop in the sea, and what forces maintain them, and whether the deep cold water from the Antarctic differs in volume from year to year and whether it is changing over longer periods. They continue, of course, to study the narrow, deep trenches, almost free of sediment, that ring the Pacific and, also, the age and cause of the mid-ocean ridges.

Another area of scientific interest is the cause, as yet unknown, of the landslides (turbidity currents) that occur in the sea, and a question of particular concern is the sudden recent increase in the radium content in cores from both the Pacific and Atlantic that date back 200,000 years.

As they seek explanations for known phenomena, oceanographers will doubtless discover new facts that need understanding. How they go about all this is well illustrated by a recent expedition in the Indian Ocean. It was the most elaborate international effort that has ever been joined in the cause of oceanographic science.

3

An Oceanographic Expedition

THE Indian Ocean Expedition of 1963 and 1964 grew out of the success of the International Geophysical Year (IGY), that ended in 1958. During the IGY more than 60,000 scientists from sixty-six nations worked at thousands of stations from the North to the South Pole, studying the earth in hundreds of different ways. In that period Russia launched its Sputnik, the United States exploded hydrogen bombs 300 miles up in the sky, and the lethal radiation of the Van Allen belt was found in outer space; but there were, as well, many beneficial results that did not have the same amount of publicity. One immediate result was to show that it was possible for many countries, although they had major differences, to unite in the peaceful pursuit of scientific knowledge.

Considering the size of the world to be measured, the cooperation of every available trained mind is necessary if it is ever to be fully understood. When the 138 million square miles of the sea are considered, it is obvious that no one country could ever afford to map all its depths and get sufficient figures about all that goes on in it.

At the conclusion of the IGY, scientists proposed that something similar to it be undertaken for the oceans. The Indian Ocean, the third largest marine body in the world, was chosen because practically nothing was known about it. For that reason, the classic book on marine science, Sverdrup's *The Seas,* gives it only a few pages. What has been called the Forlorn Ocean offered a rare opportunity for nations to work together in exploring almost virgin territory and perhaps in finding new sources of food in the sea for the undernourished peoples who live along its shores.

The program was organized under UNESCO, the scientific and cultural branch of the United Nations. Thirteen countries, including the USSR, France and Great Britain, sent ships on the expedition. Ten other countries sent observers. The National Science Foundation in Washington put up $20 million for the project. Through various government bureaus and scientific institutions partly sponsored by the government, the United States sent seven ships, which spent four times as many ship-months in the region as those of any other participating nation. Four Weather Bureau airplanes, on leave from Miami during the off-hurricane season, and a number of shore-based scientific parties also joined the project.

Among the questions to be answered were: What was the origin of the Indian Ocean basin? What forces are shaping it today? How does the crust of the earth differ here from that elsewhere on earth? What buried mountains, trenches, and rifts does it contain? What are the temperature, salinity, and chemistry of the water? How abundant is life in the ocean, and what causes the occasional massive fish kills known to occur there?

The expeditions were timed to correspond with the season of the Indian monsoons—winds that blow inland from the sea in summer, as the sun moves north of the Equator. The rapid warming of the air produces a low surface air pressure and winds that blow steadily northward along the coast of Africa and then across the Arabian Sea, picking up enormous amounts of heat and water vapor from the oceans. Over the land, the water vapor forms clouds that may reach 50,000 feet in height, so that heavy rains fall on the land. The monsoon system also acts to inject vast amounts of energy into the atmosphere above India, affecting temperature and air circulation throughout that area and probably over the entire northern hemisphere. In winter the air over the continent becomes colder than over the sea, and the wind direction is reversed. The monsoon in winter is much weaker than in summer because the immense barrier of the Himalayas keeps the cold air of central Asia away from the Indian Ocean. The reversal of air circulation between winter and summer occurs over no other ocean on so large a scale. Because this phenomenon had been very little studied, meteorology was an especially important phase of the expedition.

As evidence of the rapidly increasing world interest in oceanography, three new ships, all specially designed and built for scientific work, were available in time to make a first major voyage to the Indian Ocean. These were *Meteor,* jointly sponsored by a number of institutions in West Germany; *Discovery,* operated by the National Oceanographic Society of Great Britain; and *Atlantis II,* originating at Woods Hole. All three bore the names of previous oceanographic vessels, though none of their forebears had originally been designed for that purpose.

THE VOYAGE OF *Atlantis II*

Atlantis II is actually the third ship to bear that name; the first *Atlantis* had been a yacht. When it was sold, the name was given to a larger sailing ship that had been bought as the beginning of the Woods Hole fleet. This, in turn, was retired when *Atlantis II* reported for duty; the latter is now the largest research vessel operated by any private institution in the United States. It should be added that the funds needed to build her were furnished by the National Science Foundation.

Air-conditioned and weighing 2300 tons, *Atlantis II* can cruise for 8000 miles at a speed of twelve knots, carrying twenty-five scientists and a crew of twenty-eight. She has propellers forward as well as aft, making it possible to turn about sharply. Such tight maneuvers are often essential for handling bulky equipment that goes over the side. *Atlantis II* also has an underwater observation chamber in the bow, from which six men can gaze out at a time. The ship contains four laboratories and hundreds of thousands of dollars' worth of scientific equipment, as well as special deck gear for lifting it all in and out of the water. In heavy seas equipment can be lowered through the bottom. The ship is designed to work anywhere in the world, from fringe ice to the tropics.

Atlantis II left Woods Hole for the Indian Ocean on July 5, 1963, and steamed directly to Monaco for a courtesy call at one of the earliest homes of marine science. En route through the Mediterranean, at the request of the French Navy, her crew lowered 1800 drift bottles in the hope of producing new information about the current. Upon entering the Red Sea *Atlantis II* found a message from the Royal Research vessel *Discovery,* which had arrived there first and had rediscovered what is now referred to as the "hot spot in the Red Sea," and also as the "funny water," a phenomenon noted by the first *Atlantis* in 1958. *Atlantis'* depth recorder had encountered an unusual salinity and, upon testing, the deep water was found to be lifeless as well as extremely salty, with a temperature that registered 77° Fahrenheit before the thermometers burst. Because of its schedule, the ship had not stayed long enough to investigate fully. Now, five years later, *Discovery* had confirmed what *Atlantis* had found: a complete absence of normal organisms at a depth of 2400 feet, and at 3000 feet a temperature of 70°. The approximate temperature in the Atlantic at the same depth and latitude would have been 41° Fahrenheit.

Arriving at the location, on the same parallel as Mecca but out of sight of land, *Atlantis II* investigated to a depth of more than 6000 feet, and with specially designed thermometers found water with a temperature of 135°. It was ten times saltier than ordinary sea water. There was no oxygen in it at all, and it was loaded with heavy metals—100,000 times greater than the normal concentration. This strange water was found at the bottom of three different basins, each about five miles long and two miles wide. They ran in a line just slightly diagonal, from northeast to southwest. The "hot spot" lies quite inert, and does not mix with the normal sea water above it.

There is, of course, considerable speculation about how this extraordinary water got there; nothing like it has ever been observed anywhere else. Perhaps it is fossil water left somehow from a time before there was life on earth. It could be volcanic in origin. The three basins lie along the Rift, the same deep cleft that runs from the Dead Sea south into Africa, and perhaps it has some connection with the same deep sources of heat that produce volcanoes at points along the Rift. Whatever causes the "hot spot," it made for excitement aboard *Atlantis II,* and speculation about it will no doubt go on for years. The German oceanographic ship *Meteor,* passing later, also had a look, and found water even hotter than *Atlantis* had.

Much as the crew of *Atlantis II* would have liked to stay in the Red Sea, it had a schedule, and, since ships are expensive to operate, schedules must be followed.* The real purpose of the trip was to share in a complete survey of the Indian Ocean, including descriptive, physical, chemical, and biological oceanography; meteorology; geology; and geophysics, as well as analysis of the water and mapping of the ocean bottom.

Once in the Indian Ocean, *Atlantis II* made 227 stations, testing all the way from the surface of the sea to the bottom. In addition, water temperature, salinity, and oxygen content were read many thousands of times. Several thousand bottles were filled from the sea to get samples of the microscopic life there; daily meteorological observations were made; floats were sent out to trace currents.

None of these measurements means much unless you know exactly where you are when you take them. Accurate navigation is therefore very important, and much greater accuracy is needed aboard oceanographic ships than aboard commerical ones. Although *Atlantis* had all the latest navigational equipment, including that for taking fixes on satellites, one of its jobs during the voyage was to test a new VLF (Very Low Frequency) system enabling the ship to place itself by means of radio signals coming from Rugby, England, and from Washington, D.C., respectively 5000 and 9000 miles away. The equipment proved so incredibly accurate that the scientist in charge of it was able to show the captain of the ship, a man of considerable experience, that he was off in his reckoning by several miles. The value of such equipment arises from the fact that a ship idling on station can drift several miles from its presumed position without anyone's being aware of it. The VLF equipment is nicknamed "The Clock," and is indeed, a very superior chronometer.

* In estimating the costs of oceanography, someone came up with the figures that a temperature measurement comes to about $7 a number and that a sea-water sample captured in a bottle comes to $11 a fifth.

Along with all the other ships in the program, *Atlantis* made observations at several particular points designated for the survey, so as to provide a check for accuracy, and ultimately to set up very precise international standards for oceanographic work.

While traveling, *Atlantis II* measured the Somali Current off East Africa and found that it had one-fifth the volume of the Gulf Stream. This rather odd current is the only one known to cross the Equator—something that in theory ought to be impossible owing to the rotation of the earth. The ship also made the observation that all the atlases had shown the deep currents going the wrong way. Instead of running counterclockwise around the basin as the books said they did, the new observations indicated that they went in exactly the opposite direction. This was a finding of major importance to anyone trying to verify a uniform theory of ocean currents around the world.

Atlantis stopped at Bombay, Colombo, Zanzibar, the Seychelles Islands, Mauritius, Lourenço Marques, and Capetown, and the crew went ashore for a few hours at St. Helena in the South Atlantic, where Napoleon died. Then, in a briskly following sea, the ship headed for home, stopping to take some water samples for a British oceanographer, to make some shallow stations off Brazil to aid another colleague, and at Barbados for fuel. After a hard-working trip of 30,000 miles it arrived at Woods Hole, sheathed in ice, at one-thirty the morning of December 20, 1963.

In 1965 *Atlantis II* was once again in the Indian Ocean. The diary of the geologist C. D. Densmore gives something of the flavor of the voyage:

On the twenty-second we hauled up to the northwest, to the mouth of the Gulf of Oman, to rendezvous with the German *Meteor*. At noon on the twenty-third, at 23° North, 61° East, a helicopter came clattering over, and there was *Meteor* rolling her rusty sides a half mile away. We sent them fifteen free-fall corers by their workboat, and most of our crew went along. [These corers had just been developed at Woods Hole, and much simplified the problem of sampling the bottom.] By the time twenty Germans came over the side, I was the only scientist around to tour them. We gave them our 60° [Centigrade] thermometers for the hot water holes in the Red Sea. They were going to work the Persian Gulf a bit before heading home.

Later, I went across to *Meteor*. She is much bigger than *Atlantis II,* has twice our crew and the same number of scientists. They live opulently—carpets in the cabins, room stewards, window boxes, wood paneling. The labs are set up in European style, with dozens of small rooms off a mile of corridor, with perhaps two men in each. Many of them seemed to prefer our communal labs, as I do, and were rather wistful for our "family" ship.

We wanted their beautiful echo-sounding system and they wanted our satellite navigation. It was astonishing how rapidly opposite numbers sorted themselves out, meteorologist with meteorologist, radio with radio, mate with mate. I almost sold a geologist on my theory on the formation of Red Sea "funny water."

I always thought *Atlantis II* was cluttered, but *Meteor* looked as though they had dumped all the oceanographic gear in West Germany in a pile and built a ship around it. We did well with this bucket, thank you, and she is well kept up. We parted company at dark, tired and happy. For hours afterward, the water seethed with millions of small flying fish. We never saw anything like it. Caught a big shark with six pups.

Life at sea . . . a meeting of the scientific community . . . perhaps the Indian Ocean expedition will do something for the brotherhood of man.

Other Indian Ocean Voyages

The Scripps Institution backed three cruises during the expedition. The first involved the research vessel *Argo,* which during 1960 and 1961 carried on two-ship seismic refraction work with an Australian vessel in the waters between Australia and Indonesia.

The following year, *Argo* went out with the Scripps vessel *Horizon* on a trip that took her across the Indian Ocean three times, with stops in Singapore, Ceylon, Mombasa, Port Darwin, and Capetown, among many other places. In 1964 *Argo* went out again on a five-month cruise, mostly in the central Indian Ocean, where the ship concentrated on stratigraphy (the shape of the sea bottom), geochemistry, and the heat flow from the sea floor itself.

The Lamont Geological Observatory at Columbia University sent its *Vema* on four cruises. The first, in 1962, verified the existence of a mountain ridge and an associated rift valley first found by an expedition aboard the same ship in 1958. The ship also towed a magnetometer to chart the intensity of the earth's magnetic field. Forty-seven bottom cores of sediment were taken, and two deposits from the Paleocene era (110 to 60 million years ago) and the Cretaceous era (60 to 50 million years ago) were found. Bottom photographs were taken along with all the usual oceanographic tests. The ship also cooperated in seismic shooting with the Australian naval vessel *Diamintina.* In 1962 *Vema* returned, cruising from Capetown to Australia, then going south of that continent to dredge the sea bottom for sediment, in order to compare its thickness with that found in the Atlantic. *Vema* went back to the Indian Ocean in 1963 and 1964. During the latter trip she exploded a one-pound charge of TNT as an experiment; three hours and forty-five minutes later, the sound was picked up successfully by listening gear off Bermuda.

Other United States ships operating in the area during the expedition were *Chain,* from Woods Hole, which concentrated on physical and chemical problems; *Te Vega,* a 135-foot two-masted schooner from Stanford University, which spent a year primarily on biological studies; and *Anton Bruun,* owned by the National Science Foundation.

During the administration of Harry S. Truman, *Anton Bruun,* as the USS *Williamsburg,* had been the Presidential yacht. When the ship was converted into an oceanographic research vessel, it was renamed in honor of a Danish scientist who died suddenly in 1961. Dr. Bruun's main interest had been in marine animals, especially those inhabiting the deep trenches. He had been in charge of the Danish ship *Galatea,* which made a round-the-world cruise from 1950 to 1952. He had also been instrumental in bringing together the international oceanographic group that sponsored the Indian Ocean Expedition—hence the gesture of naming a ship after him.

Anton Bruun arrived in the Indian Ocean in 1963, and remained until the fall of 1965. During that time, Bombay was the home port of the 1700-ton vessel, which served as a national facility for many American institutions, universities and federal organizations. The ship stayed in the area, and American scientists flew out to join the party aboard during one of its scheduled cruises. There were almost always foreign oceanographers aboard, too.

The ship is primarily concerned with biological work. Scientists aboard have studied the nutrient value of sea water, and have obtained plankton samples from the surface down to 6000 feet. The amount of plankton available pretty much determines the number of fish to be found in an area. Plankton thrive particularly in the cold water that has welled up from the bottom of the sea, bringing nutrients with it. The Indian Ocean expedition was deliberately timed for the monsoon season because it was thought that this might be a time for upwelling, a phenomenon whereby the surface water is driven elsewhere and the cold water rises in its place. Upwelling was observed at various times of the year off the coasts of

Thailand and Indonesia, and it was suggested to the governments of those countries that it might be worth their while to investigate the establishment of fisheries there.

Anton Bruun has sent millions of specimens of plankton from the Indian Ocean to the Smithsonian Institution in Washington, D.C., where taxonomists sort, classify, and identify them. In addition, it has sent unusual sponges and coral, and some spectacular kinds of lobster. The rarest finds were three different species of sea snakes, much more venomous than snakes found on land. Working with men from the Bureau of Commercial Fisheries, *Anton Bruun* also discovered new fishing areas of potential importance off Mozambique, Kenya, and eastern Arabia. The animals there were mostly varieties of lobster, shrimp, and crab. The ship's ichthyologists have also sought for marlin and tuna. Six tuna were caught not far from Bombay, but the Indians at the port to whom they were offered as a gift refused them, not knowing what they were or what to do with them.

After a cruise aboard *Anton Bruun* in 1964, Dr. John Ryther of Woods Hole reported on a basic question of the expedition—the massive fish kills in the Indian Ocean. They appeared to be the result of overproductivity. Under certain wind conditions, subsurface water extremely rich in inorganic food, but low in oxygen, is brought to the surface. This causes a tremendous increase in the plankton population, and many larger animals and fish move into the area to feed. At the same time the plankton die, sink, and decompose. The decomposition uses up what oxygen is left in the water, and the trapped fish are asphyxiated—a classic instance of the effects of overpopulation.

During the Indian Ocean expedition, three new submarine canyons were found. The equatorial Cromwell Current of the Pacific and Atlantic was sought, but only a faint trace of it was discovered in the Indian Ocean. There were also studies of the Carlsberg Ridge, which runs down from the Arabian Sea to join the Mid-Atlantic Ridge off the Cape of Good Hope, and then to join another ridge that encircles Australia. The Carlsberg rises from 10,000 to 11,000 feet above the ocean floor but remains 2000 to 3000 feet below the water's surface.

Another matter for investigation was the Seychelles Islands, 700 miles to the east of Africa and surrounded by 12,000-foot depths. Their most peculiar feature is that they are made of granite, which is otherwise found only on continents; yet the Seychelles are almost certainly no part of the African continent. Remote and unique, the islands are shown by potassium-argon dating to be about 600 million years old. It has been suggested that they may be proof of the theory of the continental drift, first proposed in 1912 to account for the observation that South America and Africa would fit together along their respective continental shelves as neatly as parts of a jigsaw puzzle. According to the theory, they were once joined, until some tremendous force split them apart. It has also been conjectured that the Seychelles may be an embryonic continent whose development in some way became arrested. If so, a study of their geology might provide a clue as to how the continents came into existence.

The *PIONEER* Expedition

In 1964 the United States Coast and Geodetic Survey sent one of its handsomest ships into the Indian Ocean, on a trip that was part scientific, part public relations. This vessel, the 2500-ton *Pioneer,* had been a Navy torpedo-boat tender during World War II and was later converted into a floating laboratory. Before sailing from San Francisco, the ship was provided with thousands of illustrated booklets, to be given to visitors who came aboard, showing the various methods used to measure currents, to collect water samples from depths as great as five miles, to record water temperatures, to obtain rocks and sediment from the bottom, to photograph and map the bottom, and to measure the earth's magnetic field and the acceleration of gravity. Its work was described thus by Dr. Harris Stewart of the Survey at a Congressional hearing:

The ship worked from the upper atmosphere where the meterological balloons finally petered out, down through the surface waters where plankton tows and productivity measures were made as part of the biological program, on down through the deeper water where our water sampling profiles were tied in with the international effort to understand the circulation and distribution of variables in the equatorial regions of the Indian Ocean. The work we did tied in with the work of other ships from other countries and from the United States.

The main part of our work, however, was involved in geology and geophysics. This involved sediment coring, rock dredging, bottom photography, diving, work with heat probes, continuous echo sounding, or hydrography. It included special work with a sub-bottom acoustic device for penetrating the bottom and giving us returns from the layers below the bottom. It included the whole gambit, really, of oceanographic activities.

Dr. Stewart had been impressed with the cooperation of oceanographers from many American agencies "on the wet deck level," and the value of having local marine scientists working on board *Pioneer* as it traveled from port to port. In each port, two days of scientific seminars were held. The Americans were not allowed to "scatter about the town as tourists." Instead, open house was held and interested people —all the way from schoolchildren to government officials— came aboard and were given guided tours. Dr. Stewart felt it was important to let people in the area know what they were doing, so that "as the work does not just come back to the

United States but filters out to other countries and helps them in their fishery, meteorological, and other scientific problems." He believed that expeditions like this should be used "to help burnish up the American scientific image in a part of the world that is currently in a lot of trouble."

What Dr. Stewart did not mention about this voyage of *Pioneer* was its important discovery of a vast undersea valley, 600 miles long and 25 miles wide, surrounded by towering mountain peaks, in the Andaman Sea between the coasts of Burma and Sumatra. This rift valley is similar to the one that extends along the center of the Mid-Atlantic Ridge. Both rift valleys were formed after the action of volcanoes had caused the earth to rise and then settle in a drastically different formation. The Andaman and Atlantic rifts are alike in that both are in active earthquake zones and that both are more than a mile beneath the sea. In each zone, part of the mountain range is visible at some points above the sea—as the Azores and Iceland in the Atlantic, and as Sumatra, Java, and Timor in the Indian Ocean.

The Andaman valley is about as long as the distance between Chicago and Washington, D. C. Enormous mountain peaks tower on both sides of the valley, which is 25 miles wide. One of these rises 12,000 feet above the bottom, but it is hidden under 3000 feet of water. The floor of the valley is covered by a layer of muck and ooze half a mile deep, poured there over many hundreds of centuries from the mouth of Burma's Irrawaddy River.

The picture of the bottom of the Indian Ocean that emerged finally from the multinational investigation is a highly complicated one. Its most prominent feature is the Mid-Indian Ocean Ridge, with its deep rift down the center. The ridge begins off the continental shelf of the Arabian peninsula, and runs southeast to a point midway between Ceylon and Madagascar, from which it runs due south for

1800 miles to a position about 30° below the Equator. There it splits into two mountain ranges, one running west below South Africa, where it joins the Atlantic Ridge, and the other lying to the east and south of Australia.

Another ridge, entirely unsuspected before this expedition and called the Ninetyeast, runs on that parallel almost exactly straight from 10° North to 32° South, a distance of 2600 miles. At its southern end the Ninetyeast Ridge meets the Diamintina fracture zone, a trench that runs almost due east from Australia.

The Mid-Indian Ridge is cut by many fractures that also run in a north-south direction. These are mostly parallel with the coast of Africa, and have been named the Mozambique, Prince Edward, Malagasy, Amsterdam, and Owen fractures. In addition, there are east-west trenches such as one not too distant from Madagascar that was named for the ship *Vema.*

Other prominent features are the canyons of the Indus and Irrawaddy rivers. Yet another is the deep ridge and trench, a continuation of the Andaman, that parallels the southern coastlines of the Indonesian islands. The Indian Ocean is now known to contain many smaller rifts and trenches, seamounts, plateaus, plains, and rises. It may be many years before scientists can say with any confidence what all these mountains and valleys under the sea indicate about the past and future of the earth.

It takes times to process oceanographic observations. There is a crack in the Pacific sea floor, about fifteen miles wide, that runs for about 800 miles between Vancouver and the Aleutian Islands. The fourth such crack to have been found in the area since 1956, it is believed to have been caused by an upheaval that took place about 50 million years ago. The discovery, made by scientists aboard *Pioneer* in 1963, was not announced until 1966.

4

Men in the Sea

IT is astonishing how recent are even some of the most elementary scientific discoveries about the sea. The United States Navy took no official interest in oceanography until just before the beginning of World War II. As the story is told at Woods Hole, it all began with a letter Columbus O'Donnell Iselin wrote to Washington in 1940, after he had made a number of discoveries about temperature and salinity during summer cruises aboard his sailing ship. In his letter, Iselin is supposed to have asked if the Navy realized that a submarine could hide behind a thermocline and remain undetected by sonar gear. To which the Navy is supposed to have written back that it had not known this but was certainly interested.

According to the Navy's version, it had known, having made the discovery from submarines working in the sun-warmed seas off Guantanamo—and, knowing also of the research at Woods Hole, had gone to the laboratory for assistance. In any event, the laboratory was engaged to do wartime research in the undersea propagation of sound, and the United States Government has been doing research in oceanography ever since.

Work under the sea in submarines, of course, has a much older history. Leonardo da Vinci wrote in his notebooks: "There is too much wickedness in the hearts of men to justify my entrusting them with the secret of underwater navigation. They would not hesitate to use it to sow murder in the depths of the seas." Although that most universal of engineers kept his secret, other men later began to discover it for themselves. During the American Revolution a man called David Bushnell developed the *Turtle,* a submarine that carried a torpedo. A few years later Robert Fulton invented a submarine vessel that he named *Nautilus,* but he was unable to interest the authorities in it. These submarines were both man-powered, as was the Confederate vessel *R. L. Hunley,* a thirty-five-foot boat that required eight men to turn the propeller shaft. One night in 1864 the *Hunley* fired her torpedo along the flank of the USS *Housatonic* off Charleston and both vessels sank when the *Housatonic* blew up. A distaste for suicide missions delayed further development in America for some years.

In 1878 John P. Holland, an Irish patriot who had emigrated to the United States, built a submarine that ran on steam. When the heat from the steam proved intolerable, he used funds supplied by Irish revolutionaries to build another, the *Fenian Run,* that was powered by oil, with the intention of crossing the Atlantic to sink the British navy. The craft did have a number of successful runs in New York harbor, carrying three men down to depths of sixty feet and staying there for an hour, but it never got to England. In 1898 another craft called the *Holland* was built, and after testing it the skeptical Navy bought its first submarine and ordered six more.

The first French submarine was the successful, though fantastic, invention of Jules Verne, sailed by Captain Nemo in *Twenty Thousand Leagues Under the Sea.* The first French submarine actually built was the *Gustave Zédé,* built in 1893 and the next was the *Narval,* which could recharge its batteries at sea, using oil-powered generators; by 1900 the French had four. When the Germans produced their first submarine in 1907, they used plans for the *Aignette* which they had stolen from the French.

During World War I, German submarines became such effective weapons that they nearly defeated Great Britain. Month after month, they sank hundreds of thousands of tons of shipping. The United States' participation in the war came about largely because of moral indignation over submarine warfare and its threat to freedom of the seas. The destroyers used in fighting submarines had primitive listening gear, but the subs were most vulnerable at the time they attacked because they had to break the surface with a periscope in order to sight their victims before firing a torpedo. During World War II, German submarine action in the Atlantic and American submarine action in the Pacific were both very effective, but so were the anti-submarine measures in which the various navies made use of oceanographic science.

Nuclear Power

Among the discoveries of the war, the one that the temperature, salinity, and turbidity of sea water affect sound transmission through it has already been mentioned. Another was that schools of fish, and large animals such as whales, could be mistaken by sonar gear for enemy craft. Many an innocent marine creature was fatally surprised by a depth charge.

At the end of the war, the realization that there was still a great deal to be learned about the sea led to the establishment in 1945 of the Office of Naval Research. The Navy remained the principal source of funds for basic ocean research until the National Science Foundation was established in 1950.

Another stimulant to the federal study of oceanography has been the Atomic Energy Commission, which for some time had the notion that there were quiet waters deep in the sea into which cans of lethal debris could be safely dropped. The demonstration that hardly any ocean waters are quiet, that organisms live at all depths, and that deep currents are little understood has now made it clear that there is no national garbage dump in the sea. The folly of the idea of using the ocean for a radioactive dumping ground has been, it is hoped, thoroughly exposed as a formula for race suicide.

In return for its financial support, the Navy has now learned a considerable amount about routing ships around heavy seas, about predicting the environment of anti-submarine battles, and about submarine detection systems. With the development of atomic submarines such as *Nautilus* and of missiles like the Polaris, the Navy reached the conclusion that even giving fairly large amounts of money to private institutions was not enough, and that to use these new weapons properly it would have to step up its own research.

Nuclear submarines not only can go deeper than ever before, in the way that jet planes can fly higher and higher, but can stay underwater for two and three months at a time, and have done so. These modern submarines also travel at very high speeds. Just how high is again secret information, but they can probably outrun any surface vessel if only because they have no waves to fight. Such speeds, of course, make detecting them more difficult.

Since the United States is able to develop such vessels, it seems likely that other nations, particularly the USSR, can and have done the same. As the nation's first line of defense, the Navy must be able to detect such submarines, no matter how complicated the behavior of sound might turn out to be. What makes ocean study of such great military importance is the cloak of concealment provided by a medium which is virtually opaque to all forms of energy except sound. A Government publication, *Oceanography: The Ten Years Ahead,* puts the matter this way:

Everything we learn about how to hide our Polaris boats from the enemy's detection contributes . . . to our knowledge of how best to go about finding his.

When it is realized that sound not only travels five times as fast in water as it does in air but, for a given source, intensity produces pressures which are some sixty times as great, it is not surprising that such ordinary sounds as the singing of rotating propellers and the swish of bubbles and eddies in the passage of a hull through the sea, all of which seem comparatively short-range to a listener on land, suddenly assume tremendous significance when the sound source is in water and the listener has "underwater ears."

One particular area of concern for the Navy is that lifeline to Europe, the North Atlantic, and especially the Gulf Stream, where very many phenomena that affect anti-submarine warfare are imperfectly understood.

The deep ocean water is composed of many different temperature layers, and men have heard submarines from hundreds of miles away by listening in on certain layers favorable to long-distance transmission of sound. In a recent experiment, sound transmitted through the sea from Australia was heard on the east coast of the United States, a distance of 12,000 miles. It seems clear that if the United States is to be secure from underwater attack, its Navy had better know all it can about conditions below the surface. A Russian scientist has recently said, "The nation which first learns to understand the seas will control them. And the nation which controls the seas . . . will control the world."

The Complicated Sea

As military understanding of the sea has progressed, it has been found that the sea has its own weather much as the sky above it does. Just as in the air, differences of temperature produce currents, upwellings, and turbulence that are often very difficult to understand and to analyze. Like the land, the ocean bottom receives some heat from the earth beneath it, particularly in volcanic areas; and the sea has its own version of clouds, cold fronts, storms, and jet streams that affect the underwater movement of ships, their detection, and the trajectory of missiles fired against them.

In addition, it is now understood that the bottom slopes deflect sound and cause errors in detecting distance and direction. The composition of the sea floor has become important because it changes the reflection of sound—clay, for example, does not reflect sound as well as sand.

A matter that has required special study since the Navy began to consider building permanent installations deep in the sea is that of turbidity currents. These are underwater landslides, avalanches of sediment that charge down the continental slopes with the speed of express trains. They have caused many troubles with undersea cables, and could easily bury an installation built in the wrong place.

Another part of the problem is the nature of the bottom itself. What can be told from samples about its weakness or strength? Is it stable, or will it slump if there is an earthquake nearby? What will strong, dense currents do to a structure? What will the intense pressure do? There is also the fact that deep-sea water is more corrosive than sea water at shallow levels, since added to the chemical reaction between salt and metal there are the biological effects of sea animals and species of bacteria whose growth is not hampered by pressure, cold, or lack of oxygen. To study all these conditions the Navy has placed a number of submersible test units, variously made and equipped, on the bottom of the sea at depths of thousands of feet, to be left there for several years. The problems both of finding the units again and getting them aboard ship (one weighed almost five tons) were formidable, but a great deal has been learned from the experiments about what materials can best withstand the physical, chemical, and biological onslaughts of the deep ocean.

Measures to predict and deal with all this complexity and obscurity are the present order of the day. The year 1958 seems to be the one in which the Navy, and the federal government in general, became urgently aware of the importance of oceanography. Since the Navy did not have enough ships of the right kind for the needed research, existing ships were converted for scientific work, a number were made available to private oceanographic institutions, and ten new oceanographic ships, the first the Navy had ever built especially for the purpose, were ordered. By 1965 two of the special ships had been delivered, and the Navy's oceanographic fleet consisted of twenty-five vessels, including one submarine, the *Archerfish.*

The Naval Oceanographic Office

In 1962 the Hydrographic Office of the United States Navy, in charge of producing maps of the sea, became officially known as the United States Naval Oceanographic Office. Founded under the nation's first oceanographer, Matthew Maury, in 1854, its mission is "to enhance the combat readiness of the Navy by providing oceanographic and navigational data, performing or recommending related research, development, testing, and evaluation, and supporting associated programs in the fields of oceanography, mapping, charting, and geodesy" (the branch of mathematics which determines the exact positions of points on the earth, the shape and size of the earth, and the variations of terrestrial gravity).

During its first year of operation under the new name, the Oceanographic Office sent ships to take soundings in the Gulf of Siam, the Marianas Trench, the North Atlantic, and the western Arctic Ocean, as well as off New Guinea and Key West, and in the Bahamas. The soundings in the Bahamas were taken in conjunction with Great Britain in preparation for building a joint, permanently located underwater listening center. Knowledge of the bottom of the sea is so spotty at present that charts of the Bahamas previously in use had been based on surveys made in 1840.

Another project of the Oceanographic Office has been to commission a fleet of airplanes to take geomagnetic surveys and other measurements throughout the world. One of these planes was assigned to make low-level surveys off Puerto Rico and Midway Island in search of the ideal spot for the Mohole project. A total of more than a million miles was covered—yet the sea is said to be still largely unexplored.

Computers at Work

The information from all these expeditions is sent to the National Oceanographic Data Center, the repository for the whole gathering effort, federal and private, throughout the United States. In addition, the center receives reports from cooperating foreign institutions. Everything is sorted there and stored in computers for use as needed. Without such a computer center, the whole enormous research project (today costing a total of about half a billion dollars a year) would collapse from sheer weight of numbers. In 1963 the Data Center added information from 20,000 oceanographic stations to that from 235,000 stations which it already had on file. The measurements from all the stations are recorded on a magnetic tape system. It is now possible to retrieve valuable information on temperature, salinity, density, and sound speed, in a few hours, that would previously have taken months or years to tabulate. The Center currently has over five million different items of information, and these are increasing rapidly. In 1963 one experiment showed how all this will pay off.

In that year *Geronimo,* a ship belonging to the Bureau of Commercial Fisheries, was participating in Equalant, the international expedition to the South Atlantic. The ship, along with an Argentine vessel, was transmitting daily oceanographic information to the Center. The Center would check this with the historic data already taken, to determine its plausibility. The data from the two ships agreed very well.

Then, on September 19, time was available on the Syncom II satellite communication system. *Geronimo* radioed its information to another ship, the *Kingsport* (both were in the Gulf of Guinea at the time), which in turn radioed it to Washington via the satellite in orbit 22,000 miles above the earth. The data were evaluated at the Center, and it was found that the salinity deviated significantly from what would be expected in the area. In other words, either a hitherto undiscovered phenomenon was occurring or something was wrong with the chemical analysis. About an hour after the *Geronimo* received the evaluation message, the oceanographers aboard the ship found that their salinometer was malfunctioning. Once the scientist has left a station, he can never be sure whether he has made a mistake or found some new secret of the sea, unless he goes back to the same spot to check his observations, and this is very costly.

The Navy administers the Data Center for ten federal agencies, which draw upon it for essential information needed by military planners, commanders, and operational officers. Some of the information is classified, but a good deal of it is published, at cost, in atlases of sea surface temperatures, currents, and swells; in manuals for taking oceanographic observations; in tables of sea water density and velocity; in technical reports on special subjects; and in handbooks for forecasting breakers and surf, sea and swell.

The Oceanographic Data Center was first proposed in a bill introduced in 1959 by Senator Warren Magnuson, an enthusiast on the subject. The Senate passed it unanimously, but the House of Representatives did not even bring it to a vote. In 1960 it was finally called into being by executive order.

Whether or not the House thought the Data Center was necessary, at half a million dollars annually it is one of the less expensive items in the federal oceanographic budget. Of the $140 million in public funds spent by the government, something more than half goes to the Navy. Besides this, the Navy has another shadow budget, which the *New York Times* has reported to be $404 million. Just how this is spent is a matter for the Defense Department to know and foreign agents to wonder about. Part of it certainly goes to a mysterious offshoot of Columbia University known as the Hudson Laboratories, located at Dobbs Ferry, New York, which are listed in most but not all official registers of oceanographic institutions. They seldom turn up in the literature on the Navy's work in marine science. One ship, the 2800-ton USNS *Josiah Gibbs,* is listed as being operated by the Hudson Laboratories. Its research mission is "underwater acoustics." The *Gibbs*'s home port is given as New York City, but the director of the Laboratories, Dr. Alan Berman, reports it as Bayonne, New Jersey—which also has a navy yard. Dr. Berman says that Hudson, far from having only one ship, actually operates the largest oceanographic fleet in the nation. An

11,000-ton ship, at present only known as CMS 5, was delivered for operation in 1966. When Dr. Berman was asked what the public relations office of Columbia University said officially about the Hudson Laboratories, he said he doubted whether they knew what to say. For a general book about water, perhaps "underwater acoustics" will suffice.

Similarly interesting, if uninformative, reports were available about two $5 million grants the Navy made in 1965. According to *Electronic News,* a trade newspaper, the details are classified but the funds are for studies to "acquire tremendous quantities of data needed in critical areas, to enhance our combat readiness in all branches of naval warfare." Two new ships, *Arctic Seal* and *Atlantic Seal,* are being built to conduct the surveys.

Although the Navy has an understandable interest in maintaining secrecy (even some of its ocean depth soundings are classified), a considerable amount of its work is made public. Perhaps it is too difficult to conceal anything like the Naval Research Laboratory in Washington, which has 100 buildings spread over 123 acres, and employs 1200 scientists working on 400 projects—all of them, of course, finally related to the sea. There is also the Naval Ordnance Laboratory in White Oaks, Maryland, where a nine-story tank is being built to study the characteristics of underwater missile travel. This will contain almost two million gallons of specially treated, extremely clear, colorless water free of all suspended particles. It is to be airtight, so that the atmosphere can be controlled. Another fairly large naval facility is the Underwater Sound Reference Library in Orlando, Florida, said to be the most complete institution of its kind in the world. Also fairly visible are several naval laboratories devoted to biological research, particularly in California.

More Sound Research

Off the southern coast of California is an area once thought to have been pretty thoroughly covered by the work at Scripps and the naval base at San Diego, until it was suddenly realized that there were thousands of large marine organisms whose behavior was little known. Since many of their habits could affect fleet operations, the Navy has now flown a reconnaissance group of scientists over the entire area, and graduate students of UCLA are completing a census of the animal life there. The Navy also has a long-range program for the study of the porpoise, an animal with a sonar system superior to anything yet designed by man, and supports research on the subject at UCLA involving a seven-foot porpoise named Alice. The Naval Missile Center at Point Mugu, California, also owns five porpoises.

To further study sound, naval research supports a laboratory in the Bahamas which has mounted microphones and television cameras on the bottom of the Gulf Stream and the Florida Straits. The biologists can both see and hear such sonic fishes of the continental shelf as cod, sea horses, groupers, perch, jacks, grunts, snappers, drumfishes, angelfishes, and sea robins, which use the Gulf Stream as an express train in their migrations up the Atlantic coast. Scientists studying the sounds made by fishes can now differentiate among various species, and also distinguish the conditions under which the sounds are made. This will help the Navy to interpret the background noises that interfere with sonar, and perhaps an understanding of why fishes make certain noises and how they do it may prove useful for the tactics of antisubmarine warfare.

Biologically, the Navy would also like to know how fast-swimming fish overcome turbulence—which slows submarines

—and how they are able to navigate long distances with such great accuracy. Still other concerns are in "fouling," the accumulation of marine life on ships' bottoms that slows them down—a problem that has been more or less solved by the development of special paints—and how to cope with teredos, marine borers which have an unusual ability to digest cellulose, and which in the early 1920s destroyed every wooden pier in San Francisco Bay.

For the last several years the Navy has been studying the use of moored buoys in the high seas that would give most, if not all, of the same information as an oceanographic station. In 1960 an early automatic weather buoy in the Gulf of Mexico became the first of its kind to give advance warning of a tropical storm. The next year it survived Hurricane Carla and transmitted reports throughout the storm, remaining anchored in 11,000 feet of water.

Other automatic devices under development are a free-diving buoy that will go down to 20,000 feet for oceanographic data, and an unmanned research vehicle, somewhat resembling a torpedo, which will go down to 6500 feet for information and return to the mother ship on signal.

In 1964 the first NOMAD (Naval Oceanographic Meteorological Device) was placed in the sea 200 miles off Charleston, South Carolina. NOMAD can transmit simultaneously the weather at the surface and measurements in the deep ocean to radio receiving stations thousands of miles away. It reports normally at six-hour intervals, but in winds over 21 knots it reports hourly. Since 1964 seven other such stations have been delivered. In emergencies they will be the principal source of information from those parts of the world's oceans where facilities for reporting the weather are still inadequate.

In 1965 the Navy received its first advanced system for rapid gathering and analysis of data. This is now aboard the

USNS *Silas Bent,* and consists of instruments that can measure gravity, magnetism, bathymetric depth, and sea surface temperatures, and do seismic work while underway. On station it can also measure sea-water temperatures, sound velocity, ambient light, salinity, and depth. All this information goes into a computer-typewriter, and the results are almost immediately displayed on tape. For a fleet in operation at sea, the advantage of having all this information quickly is obvious. Now the Navy is working on various systems that will finally result in a continual oceanographic analysis for use by submarines and anti-submarine units, in motion and out at sea, in the same way that weather forecasts are provided today.

THE DISASTER OF THE *THRESHER*

At 0900 on the morning of April 11, 1963, the United States nuclear submarine *Thresher,* accompanied by the submarine rescue ship *Skylark,* took a position 220 miles off Cape Cod and made an experimental deep dive. *Thresher,* commissioned in 1961 and classed as the deepest-diving submarine in the world, had just been extensively overhauled in East Coast naval yards. The dive on April 11 was to test the craft's mettle as a result of its overhauling.

It is not quite certain when the crew of *Skylark* began to worry about the failure of *Thresher* to reappear, but that night the Navy in Washington admitted that something was wrong and that the depth of the water where *Thresher* was last seen was 8400 feet. The submarine carried 129 men and cost $145 million. The Navy said that there were a number of ways in which contact could be made with a submerged submarine; but no contact was possible with *Thresher.* The next day it was announced that there was little hope of any survivors, and President Kennedy ordered flags to be flown at half-mast. Admiral Rickover stated that there was no danger that the sea would be contaminated by the submarine's radioactive fuel, but a check was kept on the area of the disaster for many days. It proved negative.

Although rescue of the crew was impossible, it seemed very necessary to get at the wreckage, half a mile down, to find out what had happened so that such disasters could be avoided in the future. Locating the wreck was extremely difficult. To photograph it, according to the captain of the USS *Mizar,* who was at the scene, was like taking a picture of "a quarter on the floor with the camera suspended from the ceiling with a strong gale going through the room. Once you take a picture, you can never reproduce exactly the same tortuous path." After the disaster occurred, *Atlantis II,* which had been working in the Gulf of Maine, was hurried to the scene, as were five geophysicists from Woods Hole. Lamont Observatory sent *Conrad,* a Navy ship under its operation. These and other ships searched the bottom with all the available equipment, which included sounding gear, deep-sea cameras, and magnetometers—the latter an instrument developed for purely scientific purposes.

The difficulty was not only that the Navy had no craft that could go down to 8500 feet to do rescue work, but that it had only one vessel that could even go down for a look. This was the bathyscaphe *Trieste,* an outgrowth of William Beebe's bathysphere, which in the 1930s had descended to 3000 feet off the coast of Bermuda. The bathyscaphe, bought from its Swiss developer Auguste Piccard, had descended to 35,000 feet in the Marianas Trench, with Piccard's son and a United States naval officer as passengers. *Trieste* was sent by rail from San Diego, and a week after the accident, using a mechanical arm, it found one piece of metal that was identified as belonging to the lost submarine; it also took some photographs. *Mizar* took more photographs the following year with a camera lowered from the surface. No part of the sea had ever been photographed so extensively as the area where *Thresher* went down.

Apart from losing 129 men and an atomic submarine, the greatest cause of distress to the Navy was that nothing could be found out about why *Thresher* sank. There was a decision to build a Deep Submergence Rescue Vessel, which, when completed, would provide an all-weather, world-wide capability of rescuing personnel down to the collapse depth of any United States Navy submarine. It will be able to travel "piggyback" on a nuclear submarine and make shuttle trips to the surface, freeing twelve to fourteen men each trip. This will include operations under ice. While this is being developed, the Navy is installing new equipment to enable a distressed sub to announce its position and is training crew members to escape techniques.

At present, the Navy says that 80 per cent of the ocean volume lies beyond the reach of its operations. When the rescue system is complete, it will be able to survey and recover small objects down to 20,000 feet, and will thus be within reach of 98 per cent of the ocean floor. To recover sunken ships and other large objects, a system of collapsible pontoons will be developed, providing the fleet with a brand-new salvage capability.

Since the Navy has had only two peacetime submarine losses in the last twenty-five years, the rescue system will be given all sorts of secondary missions so that it will always be in a state of readiness. It will be used to transport divers for salvage operations, to help in building and maintaining bottom constructions, and as a tool for oceanographers to explore and exploit the ocean bottom. In the fortunate absence of further accidents, this may be the greatest benefit of the system. All its parts will be transportable by air, and by 1970 the Navy will have a world-wide system capable of reaching any disabled submarine within twenty-four hours of receiving a distress signal.

Living in the Ocean

As a corollary of all this, the Navy has now become interested in a man-in-the-sea program. Its objectives in setting up the program are to provide the ability to locate distressed submarines, effect rapid rescue and escape, carry out underwater salvage and recover objects of military importance, handle underwater equipment, and carry on research along the continental shelf.

The idea of living and working in the sea is not entirely new. The ancient myth-makers peopled the deeps with monsters and mermaids. Divers after sponges and pearls made a living for centuries in depths that still seem incredible. For the last hundred years men equipped with helmets, diving suits, and air hoses have been making dives, even though it has been a very tedious as well as dangerous venture. Though today they can go down to depths of 400 feet, most of the time underwater is spent getting to and from the job. Thus the diver at great depths may only spend about five minutes doing something useful, and if there is an accident during his return to the surface, he may become a victim of "the bends," a poisoning caused by the concentration of nitrogen in the blood. It was to avoid the diver's dependence on the heavy suit and on the hose from the surface that Jacques-Yves Cousteau developed the Aqualung. Even with this equipment, the diver can go down safely at present only to about 250 feet, and he has a very brief time to spend down there, since much of his swimming time must be devoted to returning to the surface by very slow stages to avoid the bends.

The idea of the man-in-the-sea programs is to take the atmosphere down with you. An American inventor named

Simon Lake did this in 1894, when he filled a submarine with compressed air, dived, and then opened a bottom hatch, through which he dug for oysters; he couldn't leave his air-filled chamber, however. The same principle was at work as if you were to invert a glass and plunge it under water; the captured air will keep the water out of the glass. If you build a submarine house on this principle and keep the air fresh and under considerable pressure, you can keep the bottom door open without having water rush in, and you can live there indefinitely.

Although a Navy doctor, Captain George F. Bond, proposed doing this as an experiment in 1957, the first man-in-the-sea project actually carried out was by Captain Cousteau. Following the suggestion of Captain Bond, the Frenchman had an undersea chamber built with the idea of housing two men forty feet under water for a week, during which time they would not need to, and in fact could not, return to the surface, but would be able to swim out from it in their Aqualungs, and work as far down as eighty feet for hours at a time. They would need no decompression until they finally returned to their normal world.

The chamber, known as *Conshelf I,* was lowered to a chosen spot off Marseilles, and, on September 14, 1962, Albert Falco and Claude Wesly dived down to it. While in their housing they were within constant view of the supporting vessel on the surface by means of a television receiver. Everything they said was heard by the men watching out for them. They were visited twice a day by swimming doctors, who gave them heart and blood tests.

When Cousteau went down to visit them the first day he found the two men in very high spirits. A television set brought them programs on the national network, they had a radio and a hot water shower, and hot meals—whatever menu they chose—were brought down to them in a pressure cooker.

What pleased them most was the number of hours they could spend diving without worrying about their return to the surface. One night, while they swam about, a motion picture was made of their activities.

On the third day it rained and was quite rough at the surface, but the chamber below did not move. When the divers from above appeared with lunch and mentioned the weather, the men below were uninterested. They no longer looked at television or acted in front of the cameras, though they knew they were under almost constant observation. On this day, unknown to those above, Falco made the following entry in his diary: "I'm afraid I can't hold out. The work in the water becomes terribly hard. Everything is getting too difficult." Wesly, at dinner, tried to cheer his companion and himself up by announcing that he wanted to go on strike but couldn't because the people above might cut off the air supply. The joke didn't go over very well. That night, for the first time, both men slept badly.

The day following, they ignored the commercial television, and asked for classical records and for a very simple menu. Falco's diary complained of too many visitors. He wished the two of them could be left alone, to go about their swimming as they saw fit. Cousteau, realizing they were becoming irritable, cut down the interruptions from the surface, and the spirits of the men below appeared to improve. Falco wrote in his diary, "The water is beginning to come into our grasp." He added, "I feel happy when I am alone with Claude."

Cousteau visited them for lunch on the sixth day, and brought caviar and a bottle of wine. This seems to have been the first time he noticed a phenomenon that has plagued every such experiment since. The special air prepared for life in the depths has a high percentage of helium to cut down the nitrogen content, and this has the effect of making those who breathe it sound like Donald Duck.

On the seventh day, according to schedule, the men lay down for several hours and breathed air that was 80 per cent oxygen, to prepare for their return to the surface. When they did come to the surface they were in good health, but subdued and rather shy of the world. Falco said later that, "under the sea, everything is moral."

The following summer Cousteau built a whole underwater village, at the same depth, in the clearer, warmer water of the Red Sea. With this he had a new manned submersible, the *Diving Saucer,* which was boarded from an undersea garage, and which went down to a depth of a thousand feet. This was the first time such a vehicle had been operated from a submerged base. A sort of frontier chamber was built in eighty feet of water and two men lived in it for a week, at one time diving to 330 feet without suffering narcosis. Five men in the main housing averaged thirty days each under the water and came back to the surface without apparent damage.* This adventure was recorded on film and in a book, both entitled *World Without Sun.* The film contains some of the most remarkable underwater photographs ever taken, but was at first greeted by the critics with considerable skepticism.

In 1964 American deep-sea living experiments began when Edwin A. Link, inventor of the celebrated aircraft trainer, sponsored an undersea housing project in the Bahamas. Here two men—Robert Stenuit, Link's chief diver, and Jon Lindbergh, son of the flyer—lived for forty-nine hours at a depth of 432 feet, considerably farther down than Cousteau's project. The chamber in which they lived was called a Submersible Portable Inflatable Dwelling, and the men breathed air that was almost entirely helium. They emerged from the

* Medically this experiment revealed two things, yet unexplained, but of considerable interest. Skin cuts and nicks that would have taken a week or more to heal on the surface healed in a single day in the pressurized cabin. At the same time, the men's beards grew hardly at all.

chamber many times and breathed from portable hoses but did little work, being content, in the deepest test of its kind made so far, merely with keeping alive. After they returned to the surface, nearly four days in a decompression chamber were needed to reduce the nitrogen gas in their blood to normal. Link had plans in 1966 for future working dives of 600 feet, with an eventual goal of a thousand feet.

Finally, in 1964, after the loss of the *Thresher,* the Navy authorized Captain Bond's undersea living experiment.

In July the Navy's *Sealab I* was sunk to the sea floor in 192 feet of water near the Navy's oceanographic research tower, *Argus Island,* off Bermuda. The *Sealab* experiment had been preceded by a number of tests in which a variety of animals were first exposed to various mixtures of helium, oxygen, and nitrogen. They survived fourteen days of exposure in pressures equivalent to that at a 200-foot depth. Human volunteers were put through similar tests, in air almost free of nitrogen, before four Navy divers went down to begin the twenty-one-day experiment. (One diver had been sent to a local store for provisions and, because of his curious tastes, all the divers had to subsist on for the entire test was canned Mexican food.)

Anticipating the problem of transmitting speech through the helium medium, a sort of filter designed to function as a speech modifier had been devised so that the men in the support vessel at the surface could understand those below. The problem of cold water had not been solved, however, and the divers in their "wet suits" of black rubber found the chill a handicap. The Navy personnel in *Sealab* also suffered headaches, sore joints, some nausea, and—as they did not notice themselves, but as was obvious to the men monitoring from above—a considerable slowing down of their movements.

Some personality changes among the divers were expected,

because it had been observed even before the project began that men who spend time under the sea tend to bcome imperious. This did occur; the men "talked, often without realizing it, as though they were the masters over all they survey, below and above." *Sealab I* had to be discontinued after eleven days, when there were warnings of a severe hurricane. The experiment was considered successful enough to justify another that was undertaken in 1965.

Sealab II was carried out on the edge of the Scripps submarine canyon near La Jolla, where the water is colder and murkier than off Bermuda but where there is no danger of hurricanes. The depth was 210 feet. The chamber was larger than the one that had been lowered off Bermuda, and it had quarters for ten men. Commander Scott Carpenter, the astronaut who circled the earth three times in May 1962, was put in charge. He was selected because he was an enthusiastic diver and had received "rigorous training for survival in a hostile environment." The teams of sailors and scientific men were rotated every fifteen days, but Carpenter stayed below for thirty days without sunlight.

When the divers first arrived below, their high-pitched, helium-distorted voices seemed very funny, though eventually they learned to make themselves understood. Less amusing were the ear infections they all suffered and the paralyzing cold of the 50° water in which they carried out their experiments. Commander Carpenter and Billy Coffman, a Navy torpedoman, suffered extremely painful stings from scorpionfish, but these responded to antihistamines and pain killers administered by the doctor who was a member of the party. Several near-accidents occurred while work parties were out, and the divers were fearful that when a sea lion, named Samantha, of whom they had made a pet, followed them to the *Sealab* entry hatch and breathed the pressurized air, she might go right to the surface and die of a blood clot.

But there was no such misfortune. The divers' morale was higher, and they did not suffer the slow-down in working ability that overtook the men in the first *Sealab*.

High hopes had been placed on a porpoise named Tuffy, who had been trained at Point Mugu to aid in rescuing distressed divers. At first Tuffy was shy of the divers, but he later became quite playful. He once located some men who pretended to be in trouble, but he earned the men's greatest respect by making a ninety-second round trip from the support ship to the submerged chamber to deliver the mail.

Toward the end of the experiment it seemed to the observers above that the men were becoming more and more reluctant to venture out into the water to do their work. While below, Commander Carpenter commented in an interview with a reporter at the surface: "Space is a very gentle place. Everything is very gentle. I think the sea is very tough. It is a very hard life. It is more hostile in some ways." Later, writing for *Life,* he called it a long and grueling experience, much more taxing physically than space flight, but "the most richly satisfying experience in my life." After coming to the surface, Robert A. Sheats, at fifty the oldest of the aquanauts, suffered terrible pains in the decompression chamber, where he stayed twelve hours longer than the other men; his wife had to stand in for him when medals were awarded for the project.

In spite of such troubles the Navy called *Sealab II* a success, and planned another capsule for living between 400 and 450 feet below the surface. It is expected that in the future aquanauts will be able to explore the sea at depths up to 1700 feet.

At the same time as the *Sealab II* experiment, Captain Cousteau was conducting another experiment of his own in *Conshelf III,* which was put down off Monaco at a depth of 328 feet. Six men lived in it for three weeks. This time the operation was almost autonomous, the only contact with the surface being the electrical cables that carried messages and power. Instead of using Aqualung bottles, the divers swam out to work at the end of hoses that led back to the main gas supply. One aquanaut worked steadily on a mock oil well rig for seven hours, an unheard-of feat at such depths. As a demonstration of future possibilities, the two parties of submerged men in *Conshelf III* and *Sealab II* carried on a telephone conversation at a distance of 6000 miles.

At the New York World's Fair of 1964–1965 the General Motors exhibit included a model of an undersea weekend resort hotel. It doesn't really appear, however, that living under water for long periods of time is going to be fun or entirely without hazard. (No smoking is allowed, though there is always wine in Cousteau's emplacements.) But the military uses make it obvious that the work will continue. Men like Cousteau will also pursue it, for his *Conshelfs* are the ideal way to engage in marine archaeology and free diving for the joy of it—freer than ever before from the mundane requirements of the surface. Such experiments also have an application to problems of deep-sea oil drilling, the mining of ore, and the harvesting of food from the sea. For oceanographers, a deep-sea platform is obviously a better base for work than the deck of a ship, and for an undersea weather station or as an observatory for study of marine life, it is ideal.

Manned Submersibles

All these interests are also served by the various submersibles that have been developed in the last few years. Mention has been made of *Alvin,* of William Beebe's bathysphere and of the work done by *Trieste I.* The Navy now has a *Trieste II,* capable of the greatest depths so far, and equipped with mechanical arms and three television cameras. A further development, *Trieste III,* was under construction in 1966.

Cousteau's first *Diving Saucer* has been purchased by Westinghouse and is being chartered for various kinds of oceanographic work off southern California. A newer variant, *Deepstar* 4000, built partly in Marseilles and partly in the United States, was delivered in 1965. It carries three men and can cruise at three knots. Still to come is a vessel of the same family, capable of diving 20,000 feet under the sea.

In another development, the Naval Ordnance Laboratory at China Lake, California, has developed a glass diving bubble capable of descending to 36,000 feet, the deepest part of the sea found so far. Glass will be used because it has been found to become stronger rather than weaker the more it is compressed, in addition to its obvious advantage of being transparent.

This proliferation of undersea vehicles in some ways harks back to the early days of the automobile. There is considerable variety in the means of propulsion, in the materials used to protect the hulls at tremendous depths, and in the shapes and the various capacities. *Aluminaut,* put out by Reynolds Metal, has been designed for a five-man crew and a depth of 15,000 feet. During tests in the Florida Straits, *Aluminaut* stayed down for thirty-two hours at an average depth of 1250 feet, with dives to 2750 feet. One problem encountered was that the abundance of plankton made such a back-scatter of the underwater lights that navigation had to be by sonar. Another development in Florida has been the Perry Cubmarines, made in West Palm Beach. Cubmarines are designed for a crew of four and a depth of 600 feet. As of 1966, seven had been sold to various interests. Also in operation is *Asherah,* a non-military submarine built by the Electric Boat Company for the University of Pennsylvania and the National Geographic Society, which can travel for ten hours at a speed of four knots, 600 feet under the sea. One of its first uses was on an underwater archaeological expedition in the Aegean. It has also been used in Narragansett Bay by the University of Rhode Island and by the Bureau of Commercial Fisheries off Hawaii. Deeper-diving submersibles from Electric Boat will be named *Star I, Star II,* and so on. The American Submarine Company of Lorain, Ohio, is making two submarines for recreational purposes, which are reported to be as easy to operate as a car. One model will go down to 600 feet, the other to 300 feet. The latter model sells for $8500.

Lockheed in 1966 had *Deep Quest* available in California. This vehicle can carry four men for twelve hours at 6000 feet and can stay down for forty-eight hours in an emergency. The Navy's *Moray* will carry fifteen men down to 6000 feet, and its *Deep Jeep* will go down 2000 feet with two men. A 152-foot submersible, the *Dolphin,* is also under construction.

These new vehicles, with their headlights and portholes and television cameras, and their unheard-of depth capabilities, have revolutionary implications for the future, not all of them military.

5

Oceanography—North and South

IT often seems that something has to go terribly wrong before the government of the United States is able to act: science steals in at the back door while all the government thinks it is doing is trying to protect its citizens. Thus it took what was regarded as the threat of the Russian Sputnik to set the massive space program rolling, and the disastrous flooding of the Colorado River to get Hoover Dam built. It was not until the German submarine attack in World War II that the Navy became involved in oceanography; and it is the presence of foreign fishing ships close to our shores that has brought about the newly launched basic research in fisheries. And long before that, the sinking of the *Titanic* in 1912, after a collision with an iceberg in the North Atlantic, put the Coast Guard into the iceberg-spotting business, and ultimately into oceanography.

The highly publicized disaster of losing a brand-new luxury liner led to the formation of the International Ice Patrol, operated by the United States Coast Guard. The duty of the Patrol was to report the behavior of the drifting mountains of ice that move down from Greenland every year, between the months of February and July, into the shipping and fishing lanes off the Grand Banks of Newfoundland. They are all the more dangerous because the Grand Banks during most of the season are shrouded in fog. From its ships and planes, the Coast Guard makes observations of the menace and then reports these observations by radio.

Over the years the Coast Guard has made many attempts at destroying icebergs by using shellfire and dynamite, bombing from airplanes, and painting them black so they will absorb and be melted by the rays of the sun; but nothing has succeeded except the natural melting of the ice as it comes in contact with the Gulf Stream. Now, however, individual icebergs are marked with bottles of dye fired at them with old-fashioned bows and arrows.

Icebergs are formed from the massive icecap that covers almost all of Greenland. Approximately 7000 icebergs of considerable size are formed every year, of which an average of 400 drift out to the open sea. Icebergs from the coastal waters of Greenland must drift 1800 miles before they reach the Grand Banks. A Greenland iceberg may tower 200 or 300 feet above the water and weigh a million and a half tons. The ice-breaker *Eastwind* spotted one in 1957 that rose 590 feet above sea level. Most of an iceberg's bulk, of course, is below the surface of the water.

Anticipating the drift of icebergs is the major reason for the Coast Guard's interest in oceanography. As they move south on the Labrador current the icebergs are observed and a chart is kept of their movements, so that if contact is lost when the weather is foggy—as it is a good part of the time—their position can be predicted.

In addition to past observations, the predictions involve the physics of the ocean. Since like the atmosphere the sea is a fluid in motion, the direction and strength of the water movement can be predicted by measuring its density and the weight of the water at various points in an area. This is similar to the work of the meteorologist who knows the simultaneous barometric pressure at many places and can therefore predict how the weather will move. Lacking a barometer, the oceanographer has to find the density of his medium by measuring its temperature and salinity. The differences in density are very slight, but they account for the motion of great ocean currents. Temperatures have to be accurate within a thousandth of a degree, and salinities within a millionth of a grain. Computers now reduce to minutes the hours of mathematical drudgery that were once necessary for this kind of reckoning. As a by-product, the information produced by the Coast Guard's Ice Patrol is very useful to oceanographers studying the fishing areas of the North Atlantic.

In the summer season, once the danger of icebergs is past, the Coast Guard goes exploring. Its ships often cruise up into Baffin Bay and ever farther north, where glaciologists study icebergs in their native habitat so as to discover the laws that govern their behavior. During one trip into the Davis Straits the *Northwind* counted a total of 3289 icebergs. On another voyage, *Evergree*n found the Kennedy Channel—an area between Greenland and Ellesmere Island, only 300 miles from the North Pole—ice free for the first time on record, and took samples from the bottom of that desolate part of the ocean. An oceanographic problem still to be solved in this part of the world is whether the water of the Labrador Current comes from Canada or from the melting of the Greenland icecap.

In 1961 the Coast Guard was officially enlisted into the nation's oceanographic effort. Since then it has conducted surveys of the deep sea and of the Great Lakes, and made studies of waves, of oil pollution in navigable waters, and of radioactivity in the sea. In 1965 two of its cutters, *Firebush* and *Madrona,* engaged in seismic shooting along the Continental Shelf of the Atlantic as part of a complete survey of this area.

That same summer, the *Northwind* made the United States' first oceanographic survey of the Kara Sea and the northern portion of the Barents Sea in the Soviet Arctic. The *Northwind* got within 500 miles of the Pole before being stopped by an ice pack, and then attempted the Northwest Passage across the top of the Soviet Union from the Atlantic to the Pacific. During the cruise the *Northwind* was under frequent surveillance by Soviet aircraft, and once a destroyer signaled it to "stop instantly." The challenge was ignored and was not repeated. Numerous oceanographic observations were taken, and it was discovered that the Kara Sea bottom was magnetically quite normal. This meant that it would not be suitable for mining, but that submarines could easily be detected in it by magnetic means, so that it would be difficult for an invader to use magnetic camouflage. It was also found that the water current north of the Soviet Union flows from east to west, in contradiction to the direction previously shown on charts. In its passage from the Atlantic to the Pacific across the top of the world the *Northwind* was hampered not by ice but by the presence of the Russian destroyer and bombers.

The Navy in the North

The United States Navy has also been active in studies in the far north. In 1961 a flier from its Arctic Research Laboratory at Point Barrow, Alaska, found an ice island 120 miles out in the Arctic Ocean. As compared with icebergs or ice floes, ice islands are relatively permanent structures that have broken off from thick land ice and that contain rocks and sediment so as to be easily taken for actual, fixed islands. Admiral Peary, in 1906, and Frederick Cook in 1908, reported islands of this sort in what is now known to be open ocean. The Navy had been looking for just such a base for a floating research party, and in the summer of 1961 a group was landed by plane on the newly discovered island. *Arlis II*, as it was called, was manned by Navy personnel and scientists for four years as it floated and meandered around the Arctic Ocean. It was evacuated only when it had drifted down through the Greenland Sea to within 200 miles of Iceland and was in danger of breaking up. *Arlis II* provided a very unusual platform for ice and oceanographic studies, including one involving underwater acoustics hundreds of miles away from any man-made source of noise.

Antarctic Oceanography

The Navy has also been interested in the Antarctic, where the first great United States expeditions were under the leadership of Rear Admiral Richard E. Byrd. In recent years the United States has had permanent installations in such locations as McMurdo Sound and at the South Pole itself, and most of the supply and communications have been taken care of by the Navy.

For the human race, the most important thing about the Antarctic is the amount of ice on it. It is not yet known when the ice began to form, but geologically speaking it is fairly recent. The ice is thought to have been a thousand feet thicker at one time than it is today. At present the ice sheet is seven times larger than that of Greenland, the next largest, and covers an area the size of Europe and the United States combined, to an average depth of 7500 feet. In some places it rises to more than 13,000 feet and in others it is more than three miles deep, its weight having depressed the land below sea level.

The Antarctic ice amounts to about 1 or 2 per cent of all

the water in the world—as much as there is in the whole North Atlantic—and if it all melted it would raise the world's sea levels by several hundred feet. There is enough water in the Antarctic to provide the world with rain for the next fifty years. Whether this great mass of ice is melting or growing is of considerable interest to seaports everywhere. The oceans that wash the beaches of the United States have risen from two to nine inches since 1940. Is this due to the sinking of the land, or to the melting of the Antarctic icecap? Calculations of scientists during the IGY are reassuring: at that time the Antarctic was said to be growing by the accumulation of 187 billion tons of ice every year.

To visualize the amount of ice involved, consider the Russian tractor party that climbed up to 13,000 feet on an ice plateau and discovered by seismic shooting that there was a range of 10,000-foot mountains buried 3000 feet beneath them. If the ice were removed, the mountains, relieved of their burden, would slowly rise. In the same way, Finland is gradually rising today as it recovers from the last ice age.

The frozen body of water that composes the icecap is also important to scientists because of the historical records it contains. Glaciologists can determine weather conditions going back thousands of years, because as each layer of snow was deposited, air bubbles, tiny meteorites, wind-blown pollen, volcanic ash, and radioactivity from the atmosphere were trapped along with it. Core samples are studied chemically and under microscopes, and the determination of age is helped by the known dates of events such as the explosions of the volcanic island Krakatoa and of various atomic bombs. The depth of the icecap, and its movements, are studied geophysically in much the same manner as scientists study the bottom of the sea. Ice shelves, which sometimes break off to form enormous flat-topped icebergs, are also a matter of scientific curiosity. The Ross ice shelf, which is nearly the size of France and almost a thousand feet thick, is one of the objects of study. A question still unanswered is whether ice erodes from the underside or is built up by the freezing of sea water.

In spite of all this locked-up water, the Antarctic air is as dry as that of the Sahara Desert. The weather is nevertheless ferocious: though there are only four inches of precipitation a year, the winds cause terrible blizzards. A temperature of 127° F. below zero was recorded at the Russian station at the South Magnetic Pole, and on the inland plateaus the average is 70° F. below. The Antarctic plays a major role in the world weather pattern, but so little is known about it that the work at present amounts to describing what goes on, without trying to determine the principles behind it.

Of two weather mysteries in the Antarctic that need solving, one is the "explosive stratospheric warming" between the middle of October and the middle of November, when the temperature of the atmosphere seven miles up suddenly rises by 140°. The other is the "great temperature inversion"—an unpredictable increase of temperature on the east Antarctic plateau.

The violent weather on the Antarctic continent produces the world's stormiest seas, full of ice driven outward by the pressure of the glaciers. The ocean currents flow in a generally circular motion around the land, but a large amount of near-freezing water flows northward into the warmer seas, producing a considerable effect on the weather thousands of miles away. Where these north-flowing waters meet warm waters flowing south, there is a very distinct area known as the Antarctic Convergence. The waters in the Convergence are some of the richest in plankton and larger animal life in all the world, and it was in search of whales, which flourished there, that the first navigators approached what to them was still *terra incognita.* Millions of seals and penguins and other birds, fearless because they have no natural enemies, survive the fierce weather of the Antarctic and take advantage of the abundant food in the adjoining water.

Emperor penguins have interested scientists because of a number of remarkable attributes. They breed on sea ice, they make no nests, and for an incubation period of sixty-two days, in temperatures that may be as low as 70° F. below zero, the male carries the one egg laid by his mate on his feet. During this time he eats nothing at all. After laying the egg, the female goes off to feed in the sea; she is able to time her return with the hatching of the egg, and she is also able to identify her mate even though the rookery may contain thousands of birds. She now feeds the chick while the male goes to the sea to restore the nearly half of his body weight that he has lost while keeping the embryo warm.

Just as phenomenal is the navigational skill of Adélie penguins, which have been transported in airplanes by experimenters for hundreds of miles from their nesting grounds, yet have faithfully returned over the featureless ground to the exact spot where they have been taken.

Also of interest to scientists in the Antarctic is the Weddell seal, which has chosen the coldest place in the world to live. It has the ability not only to dive a thousand feet under the water and return rapidly to the surface without getting the bends, but also to find breathing holes in a sea that appears completely covered with ice. How the Weddell seal navigates, and whether the adaptation it makes during a dive might in some way be simulated by man for his own purposes, are concerns that have caused Antarctic scientists to go down through the almost freezing water into sub-ice observation chambers to watch these animals' activities.

One of the first formal explorations of the Antarctic was made by the British ships *Erebus* and *Terror,* under the leadership of Sir James Clark Ross, between 1839 and 1843.

The purpose was primarily geographical, but there was some interest in the biology of the sea. The first reported catch of a fish within the Antarctic Circle was made at this time. According to the log kept by Sir James, "When the ships were in the high latitude of 77° 11′ south, a fish was thrown up by the spray in a gale of wind, against the bows of the *Terror,* and frozen there. It was carefully removed, for the purpose of preservation, and a rough sketch of it was made by the surgeon; but before it could be put into spirits, a cat carried it away from his cabin, and ate it."

A great number of ships have been in the area since then, but none—whether or not it had a cat—was as well equipped as the *Eltanin.* This floating laboratory for Antarctic research is the property of the National Science Foundation, which has charge of USARP, the United States Antarctic Research Program. An official pamphlet of the program describes the continent as "a vast natural laboratory affording a relatively simple and uncontaminated environment for the study of phenomena that have direct bearing on many similar and analogous phenomena throughout the rest of the world." A fair amount of the money for the program goes into operating this American vessel, which sailed south in 1962 and has not been out of the Antarctic since then except for occasional calls at Santiago, Chile.

Eltanin was built originally as a supply ship for radar stations in the Arctic. Its bows are designed to slip over the ice rather than crush it. Since *Eltanin* was intended for work in the Arctic, it had been named after a star in the far northern constellation Draco. Though the name remains, the ship's cargo holds were refitted with four new laboratories; staterooms for the scientists and large anti-roll tanks to keep the ship reasonably stable in the rough southern waters were also constructed.

A cruise on *Eltanin* is only for the rugged. Each voyage

south from Santiago lasts sixty days and consists mainly of trips north and south, each leg about 125 miles distant from the one previous, crossing and recrossing the Atlantic Convergence. Land is hardly ever seen—only cold gray skies, whitecaps, and ice.

On one voyage the scientific work included studies of the basic biology in the convergence waters, as well as of plankton, gravity, magnetism, airborne insects, radio signals from California, the geological links between South America and the Antarctic, ocean currents from the bottom of the sea to the surface, and a comparison of southern auroras with those of the north. To do all that work in such inhospitable seas takes fortitude—and a good disposition.

From the standpoint of pure oceanography, since the waters of the Antarctic circle the globe uninterrupted by continental land masses, they offer an ideal model of ocean circulation. The area is also ideal for the study of waves, which may someday lead to better wave predictions. That the winter ice cover of the area appears in effect to double the size of the continent in summer is a matter that will need accurate verification before world-wide weather predictions are possible.

The role of the Antarctic Ocean in the fisheries of the world is also very important. Not only is sea life abundant, but cold water from the south upwells to produce the rich fishing grounds off the coast of Chile and also those that have been recently discovered through oceanographic research in the Gulf of Guinea, off the coast of Africa.

Though the Antarctic seems remote, natural events occurring there set up reactions that must ultimately affect the atmosphere, the oceans, and the life in them, everywhere else in the world. That men of intelligence and learning from countries as far distant as Russia, Great Britain, and the United States have gone there shows, perhaps better than anything else, the interdependence of the whole world of water. Who knows but that the study down there of the shrimplike krill, the abundant little animal that is the favorite food of whales, may teach something that can be of use toward increasing the fisheries off North America or Europe. Or that an understanding of the upwelling that occurs in the Antarctic Convergence may make possible what is now only a fanciful notion: that heating the nutrient bottom water off southern California with a nuclear reactor, thereby causing it to rise, would not only multiply the fish population but also, incidentally, set up a breeze to drive away the Los Angeles smog.

6

The Business of the Sea

Archaeology and Treasure Hunting

MANY activities that now go on under the sea scarcely come within the definition of oceanography. The men involved use words like oceanics, ocean engineering, archaeology—or plain, outright treasure hunting. Cousteau showed the way some years ago when he excavated a ship that had sunk about the year 300 B.C. on a reef off Marseilles. It had carried 10,000 amphoras containing wine, and Cousteau's men brought a great many of these to the surface. One even had a drop of wine still in it. This can be regarded as a treasure ship, however, only by the museums that gratefully accepted the ancient artifacts. With Aqualungs and submersibles such as *Asherah,* the Mediterranean and other inland seas are easy to explore, and no doubt many shipwrecks of antiquity will be uncovered.

In the Americas, the route of the gold-bearing Spanish galleons is understandably of great interest. Among favored sites for diving are the sandbars and reefs off South American ports, the Florida Keys up to Cape Kennedy (one of the richest spots), and any area in the Bahamas and Bermuda that is dangerous for modern shipping. Navigators used to sail close to Bermuda to get a position before crossing to Europe, and many ships were lost in the reefs there. Likewise, the Florida Straits were traveled by Spanish convoys from the Caribbean to avoid the prevailing winds to the south. One such fleet left Havana on July 13, 1733, supposedly before the beginning of the hurricane season. Along with much personal treasure, the ships carried most of the silver pieces-of-eight that had been minted in Mexico for the previous two years. On July 14 a premature hurricane caught the convoy in the Straits, and eight ships were sunk. A few years ago one of these was discovered, and among the wreckage were forks, figurines, swords, muskets, pewter bowls, and glass bottles, as well as silver coins.

Another recent search of historical interest uncovered the remains of Port Royal, off shore from Kingston, Jamaica. Most of the town had been hurled into the sea by an earthquake just before noon on June 7, 1692. Divers found among the sand-covered ruins a watch in a brass case, later identified as the work of a watchmaker in the Netherlands before 1686, that had stopped at seventeen minutes before twelve—the exact moment of the earthquake.

A treasure found recently on the Florida coast between Cape Kennedy and Palm Beach led the state legislature—anxious, like any government, for its share of the wealth—to pass a new law. In 1964 a firm that called itself the Real Eight Company discovered coins and other objects, from a ship wrecked in a hurricane in 1715, which were valued at $1,860,000. The State of Florida had already been issuing special permits for this kind of treasure-hunting; but Real Eight had strayed beyond the area of its permit and had failed to give notice of the discovery, although the relics filled the vaults of three banks. The State has now declared that one-quarter of any treasure found along its shores belongs to it, and an agent is sent along during the diving to make sure what goes on. A Florida diver named John Sykes, who without any permit at all found two statues of authentic Aztec gold and $75,000 worth of coins in a wreck off Fort Myers, may eventually have to share his fortune with the State. Probably the greatest quantity of sunken treasure, although there was no secret about its location, was the shipment of gold ingots, worth almost £2,500,000, aboard the merchant ship *Niagara,* which sank off Australia en route to New Zealand in 1940. An American, J. E. Johnstone, went to work the next year with a diving bell, and recovered 555 of the 590 lost ingots—a job that took him one week short of twelve months.

Undersea diving, of course, is pursued more often for pleasure than for the hope of discovering anything from the past. All sorts of propulsion equipment to which the diver merely hangs on has been manufactured. Underwater parks have now been established, with the purpose of setting aside particularly beautiful or interesting areas that will be protected from commercialization and curio seekers. Among these are Buck Island near St. Croix, Exuma Cays in the Bahamas, Fort Jefferson in the Dry Tortugas, and the Pennekamp Coral Reef Preserve near Key Largo.

Oil from the Sea

The oil industry has aided oceanography while pioneering in explosive prospecting. By means of two-ship seismic shooting with TNT, its prospectors explore the sea bottom for the salt domes under which deposits of oil are often trapped. Wave and weather predictions are of value to the operators of tankers, the world's greatest users of the surface of the sea, and of offshore drills and wells. The men on the rigs in the

Gulf of Mexico must have felt special gratitude to the meteorologists who warned them in time to come ashore before hurricane Betsy hit the area in the fall of 1965.

The sea is inseparable from the oil industry, for although the exact process that has led to the formation of petroleum deposits is unknown, an essential step involves an immense pressure such as the oceans alone could have exerted. Thus all such deposits must at one time have been under the sea. It is known, besides, that oil exists on the continental shelves, all of which were once dry land and therefore contain the necessary organic debris. The oil industry needs geologists to tell them how to find these deposits of crude oil and chemists to tell them how it can be processed.

The first large deposits of oil under the sea were found off Venezuela, in the shallow salt-water arm of the Caribbean known as Lake Maracaibo. For many years a daily shipment of more than a million thirty-one-gallon barrels has been made from this body of water, now a forest of derricks, to the islands of Curaçao and Aruba, where the crude oil is refined and reloaded onto large tankers.

Offshore oil found in the Persian Gulf, the Arabian Sea, and Cook Inlet in Alaska, has been taken from wells as much as fifty miles from shore, in water as much as 240 feet deep. Two huge drilling units from Japan, delivered in 1965 to Borneo, rest on the bottom at 135 feet or act as semi-submersibles in water 600 feet deep and are designed to drill wells to depths of 20,000 feet. There has been a flurry of activity in the North Sea, which is all continental shelf, since the Dutch discovered natural gas under an estuary of the Ems River. More natural gas has been found near the English shore, and so the test drills continue.

In the United States the offshore oil deposits have been the cause of prolonged legal and political dispute. In 1948 the United States Department of Justice went to court in an attempt to get a clear title to all the land up to the coastline. The Supreme Court ruled in the Department's favor in 1950; whereupon the states of Louisiana, Texas, and California turned to Congress for help. In 1953 that body passed a bill granting the states the offshore lands out to the three-mile limit, or to a distance of nine miles if the state could show a historic title to justify the claim for the extra territory. Louisiana made such a claim, but the Supreme Court ruled in 1960 that its territorial limits extended only three miles into the ocean. Despite the cloud of controversy hanging over the area, American oil companies have invested more than $4 billion in offshore wells in the Gulf of Mexico. These, together with those off California, now produce about 200 million barrels a day.

Some of the labor connected with oil wells in the ocean, for example the fitting of pipes, has been handled by deep-sea divers. As the wells move into deeper and deeper water, however, this work will no longer be possible for divers. It is estimated that exploration for oil on the Continental Shelf is only about 20 per cent complete, and that the remaining wells may be in water as much as a thousand feet below the surface. The services of manned submersibles, which can work at such depths, are being offered, and no doubt they will be utilized.

The Shell Oil Company has managed, by an ingenious device, to demonstrate the existence of oil wells in deep water that no one has ever visited at all. The device is Mobot, an underwater robot controlled from the surface by television that can swim, hear, see, and work deep on the ocean floor. Developed for Shell by the Hughes Tool Company, Mobot is connected by a single cable to a ship on the surface, where a man sits at a console and moves the switches that control the motions of the robot. Through two television transmitters down in the sea, the man can observe what is taking place, and direct the robot to turn a valve that will regulate the flow of oil or to seize a wrench that will repair a piece of tubing. Using Mobot and a surface drilling rig, Shell discovered a well off the California coast near Santa Barbara and set up the machinery and pipes to bring the product ashore—all at long distance. Though Mobot had been looking for oil, what it found turned out to be natural gas. Since artesian pressure was at work, no pumps were necessary at the well itself. At the water's edge the pipes were buried under the sand and then carried underneath a highway to a receiving station hidden in a ravine. A motorist on US 101, without knowing it, can drive over a pipe that every day brings in 30 million cubic feet of gas from under the ocean.

For a time Mobot was a trade secret. When rumors began to spread through the industry, Shell's publicity department made the best of the situation by producing a film showing Mobot at work for the edification of their competitors. The film was offered as a prospectus for a course in how Mobot works. The tuition was fairly high—$100,000 per person—but twenty engineers were sent to study.

Prospecting for oil at sea adjacent to known deposits on the land makes sense and has proved worth-while. In California there are hundreds of pumping stations within the three-mile limit, where the state gets a percentage of the production. The stations are very scrupulous about pollution, all the refuse is taken ashore for disposal, and the riggings are so attractive to fish that they are surrounded by small boats full of fishermen.

Prospecting in an area that has never produced oil, known as "wildcatting," calls for daring, financial and otherwise, especially when that area is the deep sea. Oil has never been found in the state of Oregon and the sea bottom within its own three-mile limit is covered by lava deposits that are, geologically speaking, quite new. To discover whether or not there is oil beneath the deposits is a very difficult proposition. Nevertheless, a number of oil companies have been ready to pay the United States government advance bonuses adding up to about $35 million for the privilege of wildcatting farther out along the Oregon coast.

In 1965 Shell leased several thousand acres of sea bottom about eighteen miles off the town of Newport (the home of the Oregon State University school of oceanography) for test drilling. A new deep-sea rig was especially designed for the contrary winds and waves of the Pacific coast. Known as *Blue Water 2* and standing fifty feet above the water, the rig is about an acre square and big enough for a helicopter to land on its deck. At the surface, where the waves strike, only a few thin supports are visible, the actual base being twenty feet below. Thanks to a system of balances, *Blue Water 2* is able to stay in position over a drilling operation in very high seas. It does not stop operating until the waves are twenty-five feet high, and it has withstood gales of 101 knots, with thirty-five-foot waves. The first drilling off Oregon was in 325 feet of water, with plans to go down to 10,000 feet, but the test was unsuccessful, and *Blue Water 2* moved on to another likely spot in the leased area. This drilling was capped, and competitors may not know for several years what was found. The lease for the area cost a little less than $9 million, and the rig costs $15,000 a day to operate.

While the *Blue Water 2* was drilling, the company leased two ships from a geophysical surveying company for seismic shooting. Since conservationists in Oregon were apprehensive about what all that TNT would do to the fish, a state representative was always present, at Shell's expense, to see that no shooting was done where fish were evident.

Oil companies now have the capability of drilling in a thousand feet of water but very little idea what they would do if they struck a deposit. Shell is not quite sure what it will do with the oil it finds eighteen miles out at sea. The custom of the industry has been to improvise as the situation demands, and Shell's officials are confident that if they do find commercial quantities, there will also be a way of piping them in, even if they have to invent it.

Oil drilling in the deep sea has produced much of the experience needed for such projects as the Mohole. The same kind of experience may also someday show how advantage can be taken of the mineral wealth on the sea bottom.

Minerals under the Water

Companies in the mining business do not seem to have the spirit of adventure that is traditional in oil. Mining people are skeptical of the sea, they are not sure how they can establish a clear legal title to a deposit of ore for their exclusive use, and because of the enormously greater expense of working in the sea as compared to the land, they have been slow to take action. The government, knowing the amount of money it can get for oil leases, expects similar amounts for mineral rights, and the interests involved find this unfair.

The minerals are there, nevertheless, in the water itself and on the ocean bottom. Off South Africa, in the territorial waters where the Orange River, after running through the diamond country, enters the sea, a dredge is now siphoning sediment from the sea floor and panning it for gems. The world's first floating diamond mine, *Barge 77,* went into production on August 10, 1962, and before being driven ashore on the rocky coast in a storm on July 1, 1963, it had produced 51,000 carats of gem quality, rough diamonds valued at $1,770,000. At this point the De Beers international diamond trust, which had not been interested previously, went into partnership with the Americans who had begun the enterprise. The Marine Diamond Corporation, Ltd., is now substantial enough to employ a thousand men and have its own fleet of ships and airplanes. The present production rate is valued at about $15,000 a day.

Diamonds have a very high unit value, and the water in which the dredging is being done is no more than a hundred feet deep. Among other minerals in the sea, the most fascinating to many people are the manganese nodules that occur in depths of one to two miles. Manganese is necessary in the manufacture of steel, and there is not a great deal of it in the United States. Moreover, these nodules are a scientific mystery—concentrated out of sea water, no one knows how—and of very high quality. It is estimated that billions of tons of them await the picking; unfortunately, most of them are in water at least a mile deep. John Mero, author of *The Mineral Resources of the Sea,* urges the government to subsidize mining them, lest one day we find the Russians gathering them off the ocean bottom at our own front door. He points out that the nodules also contain copper, nickel, cobalt, and small amounts of lead, zinc, and molybdenum. He believes that the United States could reduce its dollar drain by more than $1 billion a year if it were to mine these deposits rather than buy the metal from foreign countries. The trouble is that whoever goes after them will meet with the same obstructions as oceanographers, divers, submarines, and oil drillers—all the problems engendered by the hostile environment deep down in the water. There are rumors that various corporations are willing to face all this—plus the admittedly enormous investment—but there have been no reports of activity thus far.

Use is being made in shallower water, and on beaches, of the minerals of the sea. After a storm, the shores of Oregon are patrolled by jeeps equipped with screens such as are used in placer mining, and many of the people operating them make a living from gold that has been carried from the mountains to the sea and then washed up during rough weather. Tin mines extend under the sea off the coast of Cornwall in England, and there is placer mining of tin on the beaches of Malaysia. Japanese coal deposits also extend under the sea. A lease has been granted for the recovery of gold off the mouth of an Alaskan river known to contain gold-bearing gravel.

The United States Bureau of Mines has recently joined with Lockheed and the International Minerals and Chemicals Corporation in a project to mine phosphate. There are said to be 60 million tons of phosphate off the coast of southern California, in relatively shallow water. California itself purchases 300,000 tons of phosphate a year for use as fertilizer. The interest of the Bureau of Mines in the project is the general one of learning how to extract whatever is of value from this challenging environment.

Discussions of the wealth from the sea are never complete without reference to the chemical elements in the water itself. Every known element on earth is there, though only salt, magnesium, and bromine are now commercially extracted. If desalinization is ever developed to any extent, some of the cost may be recovered by taking gold and other valuable minerals from sea water along with the salt—a matter of 12,000 tons for every 100 million gallons of fresh water.

Indisputably great as is the wealth in the sea, only such precious substances as oil, gold, and diamonds are being taken from it at present, aside from the basic resource of food. And the methods of the fisherman are primitive. No one is getting very rich from the industry in the United States.

Food for an Exploding Population

Today, so far as food from the sea is concerned, man is still in the hunting stage. The search for new sources in the Indian Ocean is just a sophisticated version of the ancient methods. So is the use of sonar gear to find schools of fish.

The future of the business seems to be in moving on to the agricultural stage.

One possibility for supplying food to mankind has centered around the enormous variety of algae, plants that thrive in water everywhere. The most promising of these is *Chlorella,* a genus of green algae. Properly tended, *Chlorella* grows rapidly and produces great amounts of plant material. The yield per acre is greater than that of any other agricultural crop—and it is high in protein, carbohydrates, and fats. From this material a great variety of foods can be processed. Where the population exceeds the available food supply, the culture of algae could be of enormous importance. Although it has been demonstrated that algae can be converted into quite palatable food, undoubtedly a great deal of education, particularly in such countries as India whose people are conservative in their eating habits, will be necessary before its great potential can be realized. An example of Indian conservatism is the previously mentioned bewilderment of the Indians who didn't know a tuna when they saw it.

Attempts to solve the world food problem from the sea also run into political and emotional complications. The United States recently offered to supply fish meal powder, which is extremely high in protein, as an additive to food in several countries on the verge of starvation. This was a bureaucratic blunder; nobody paused to recall that another branch of the Government had disallowed fish meal as human food—until the intended foreign beneficiaries of the program raised a storm over the fact.

A fresh-water African fish, the tilapia, similar to the American sunfish and both very adaptable and prolific, has been found to be a rich source of protein. It feeds directly on algae and plankton, as do oysters, mussels, and clams, and thus represents only two steps in the food chain from inorganic ions to protein. It is resistant to disease and can live in fresh or brackish waters. Under the sponsorship of the United Nations, the tilapia was introduced in many subtropical lands. Hopes were high until the tilapia was found to breed *too* fast, and to stay too small as a result of overpopulation. Now a hybrid—one that cannot breed—has been developed, and is being used to stock waters in many places with considerable success. Such is the process known as Aquaculture.

The Bureau of Commercial Fisheries has put out a booklet on the shrimp farming methods of southeast Asia, and how these might be adapted for use in the Gulf of Mexico. Fish farming is being carried on in Hawaii, and also in an experiment off the shore of Scotland, where heated water from power stations is being used to stimulate growth. A problem in farming fish in the sea is how to set up a barrier that will let in fresh, nutrient-filled water and yet contain the animals. Among the proposals are a sonic barrier through which fish would not be willing to pass, and a fence of air bubbles. A group in Palo Alto, California, plans to operate a farm for the steelhead trout which, like the salmon, breeds in rivers, spends its adult life in the sea, and then returns to its birthplace to spawn. A fish hatchery operated near the mouth of the Matole River will provide the steelheads with a private homing stream, unimpeded by dams. The fish will be released to the sea at controlled intervals, so that some will be returning continuously throughout the year.

Other schemes for fish culture utilize the known tendency of fish to congregate about wrecks and other bottom obstructions, where colonies of crustacea and seaweed provide food. It is thought, also, that fish take advantage of such structures as hiding places from predators. Fishermen in the Great South Bay off Long Island, where concrete apartments for fish have been built, report excellent results. Off Santa Monica, California, where the bottom is sandy and there is little to attract a permanent fish population, the State Department of

Fish and Game has set up artificial reefs in the form of abandoned automobiles and streetcars, as well as concrete structures. Kelp has been transplanted, and the scheme has been a great success. The concrete structures seem to be preferred by the fish.

Scientifically, the most important study of fish is that of plankton, their source of food. Without irrigation, weeding, or fertilizers, plankton thrives and drifts through the vast saltland prairies. Researchers want to know how and why.

They are also trying to find some way to stop the enormous wastage of fertile fish eggs. Only one per cent of the eggs survive to maturity; the rest are gobbled up. Other areas of interest are fish migrations and appetites, how they get salt out of the water they consume, whether or not they sleep, and whether they have a sense of smell. The behavior of tuna is being observed from a small submersible, and a search is on for edible species of fish that may have been neglected. Many studies are now being made of ways to catch fish, although the social status of fishing, "a poor man's industry," had once led scientists and engineers more or less to ignore it.

After World War II, when many of the world's fishing fleets were being rebuilt, a number of nations began experiments with new fishing techniques. The Russians, having discovered that a certain kind of anchovy always swims towards a source of light, invented a combination light and pump that permitted the dazzled fish to be scooped up as with a vacuum cleaner. Another Russian development has been a system of herding fish by means of underwater electric charges toward a spot amidships, where there is a suction nozzle through which they are pumped aboard. In the United States, oceanographic research has shown that there are fish in commerical quantities at depths of 3000 feet below the mouth of the Columbia River, and much work has gone into discovering how best to locate and recover the fish from deep water. Trawling equipment now available can be lowered to a precise depth—for example, exactly 1120 feet, where sound equipment may have reported a school of fish. An air-bubble technique for guiding herring has been tried out with some success in the Gulf of Maine, and other ideas for herding fish are on the drawing boards. These include using odors to guide fish, putting chemicals in the water to act as barriers, and introducing sounds of prey or predators to attract or drive them.

Research into the habits of shrimp has shown they leave their burrows between seven and eleven o'clock at night, and that the catch is much greater during those hours. It has also been shown that shrimp can be induced to leave their burrows by applying a very small electrical charge—a method that has increased catches during daylight hours. Though research findings and new techniques will be taken up fairly rapidly in the prosperous shrimp industry, there are other commercial fisheries—particularly in New England, where in many ports the archaic methods of handling fish have changed very little in the last fifty years—where the progress will be slow.

Few other countries in the world could afford the decline in the fishing industry that has taken place in the United States. From a total catch of 3.3 billion pounds in 1949, the figure had dropped to 2.5 billion pounds in 1962. During the same period, imports of shrimp, tuna, lobster, and fish meal had tripled. World-wide production of fisheries outside the United States has risen dramatically, almost doubling in the last ten years. Fishing in the United States suffers, as does the merchant marine, from wage scales that are not competitive with those of other countries. The State Department, wary of any move that might complicate international relations, has backed low tariffs and limited claims to fishing territory. American fishermen have been unable to meet the competition of Russia and Japan, whose governments give large-scale support to their fishing industries. Both countries now operate fishing fleets in the free seas all over the world, and not uncommonly within sight of United States territory. The Russians in particular have large factory ships that can process the catch while at sea.

A large portion of the increased catch has gone into the production of fish meal, which is used to feed cattle, chickens, and turkeys. The greatest increase in fishing for this purpose has been in the upwelling seas off the coast of Peru. Whereas in 1947 the anchovy catch was 31,000 tons, by 1962 the figure had risen to 6,800,000 tons.

Certain questions now arise: How long can the fishermen of the world go on increasing their haul? How many fish are there in the sea? What proportion can be taken before a species is wiped out? The blue whales of the Arctic have almost disappeared; so have the Pacific fur seals. Sardines are no longer an industry in California; salmon are becoming scarcer and more expensive. Thirteen nations are competing for the herring and cod on the Grand Banks, to an extent that navigation in the area is now dangerous. Since the seas are open to everyone, each fisherman tends to think that if he doesn't grab everything he can get, someone else will come along and take it instead. There is no incentive for conservation. There is also quite a difference of opinion about what constitutes territorial waters, and encounters between United States and Japanese or Russian fishing vessels are common, as are those between the shrimp fishermen of Mexico and the United States in the Gulf of Mexico.

International agreements would seem to be necessary if the populations of the most desired fish are not to be wiped out in the manner of the buffalo and the passenger pigeon. Agreements are very difficult, however, when no one knows what the available supply really is. Granted that fish produc-

ESSA

Oceanographer, the pride of U.S. marine science. Biggest of the new class of ships designed specifically for ocean research, and equipped with advanced technical gear, *Oceanographer* is part of the Coast and Geodetic Survey fleet.

Woods Hole Oceanographic Institut

Woods Hole Oceanographic Institution on Cape Cod in Massachusetts. Two of Institution's five ships, *Chain* and *Crawford,* are shown in foreground.

The watery world; a U.S. scientist lowers a Nansen bottle into the sea, during the 1964 Indian Ocean Expedition, to test temperature and salinity.

Science Service

FLIP (Floating Instrument Platform) stands 55 feet in the air while 300 feet of its length are submerged beneath the noisy surface. FLIP's function is to study the propagation of sound in water.

U.S. Navy

Navy Department

lvin, miniature research submarine built for Woods Hole Oceanographic Institution. esigned basically for scientific studies at depths of several thousand feet, *Alvin* helped the recovery of the lost H bomb off the coast of Spain.

Camera Haw

Keiki, the dolphin raised from infancy by ocean scientists at the University of Haw: Here his speed in the open sea is being tested; Keiki returns to the boat at the sou of a bell.

Woods Hole Oceanographic Instituti

Atlantis II at sea. Built for Woods Hole Oceanographic Institution by the U.S. Nav *Atlantis* has achieved many scientific firsts, including investigation of the Red S "funny water." The previous *Atlantis* had been a converted sailing ship.

Bruce Rogers aboard the *Anton Bruun* guides a plankton net into the Indian Ocean to collect specimens of the microscopic animals and plants, basis of the sea's food chain. The ship, named for the famous Danish oceanographer, belongs to the U.S. National Science Foundation.

National Science Foundation

Navy Department

e *Holland,* first submarine purchased by the U.S. Navy. The inventor, an Irish patriot, ilt a less successful vessel earlier, intended to sink the British Navy.

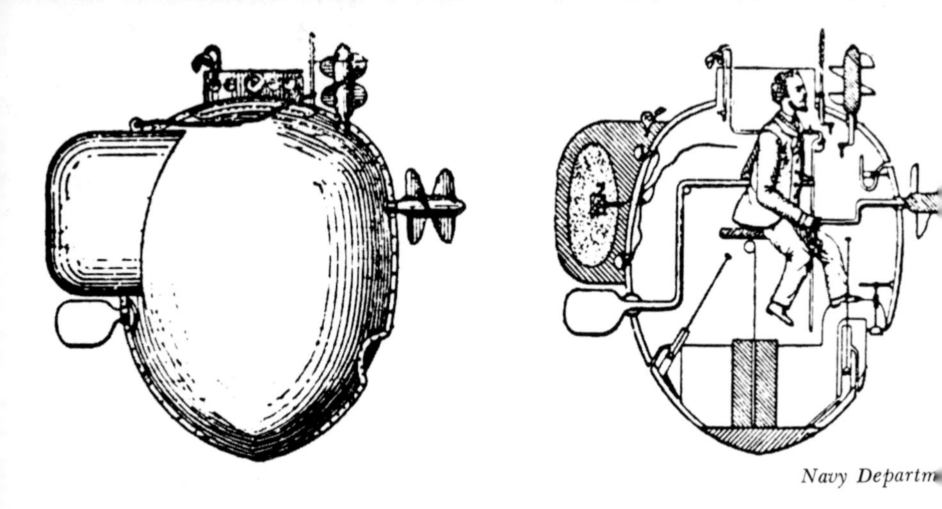

Navy Departm

Bushnell's submarine, an early attempt to navigate beneath the waves.

U.S. Navy

Sealab I aquanaut shown leaving the enclosed exit area of the habitat. The enclosu a shark cage, acts as a safety measure. The *Sealab I* experiment took place at a de of 193 feet in waters off the coast of Bermuda, August 1964.

Navy Department

'avy frogmen feeding Tuffy, the porpoise, who carried mail during the *Sealab II* ‹periment.

Westinghouse

n undersea vessel for exploration and work down to 4000 feet, Westinghouse's *Deep-ar* carries three men who are able, unlike those working from a surface ship, to see hat they are doing.

U.S. Coast Gua

On station in the stormy North Atlantic, the Coast Guard cutter *Pontchartrain* stays sea for weeks at a time to report the weather and come to the aid of distressed ships a aircraft.

U.S. Coast Gua

The Coast Guard cutter *Campbell* surveying an iceberg found northeast of Newfoun land. The ship, part of the International Ice Patrol, is unable to sink the berg, but ca track it and report its position to menaced shipping until the ice finally melts after co tact with the Gulf Stream.

N.S.F.

ancake ice forming in the Antarctic Ocean, seen from the deck of the *Eltanin,* research ip of the National Science Foundation.

he Soviet research vessel *Vityaz,* at anchor in the Seychelles. These Indian Ocean ands are a curiosity because they are made of granite, a structure found elsewhere ly on continents. *Vityaz,* built specifically for oceanography, has many deep-sea disveries to her credit.

Miami Daily News

An autumn hurricane batters the seawall at Miami's Biscayne Bay. Improved warning systems have greatly reduced loss of life caused by these storms.

An experiment in weather modification. At Yellowstone Park a can of water is thrown into the air in a temperature of 45 degrees below zero, and produces a cloud of ice fog.

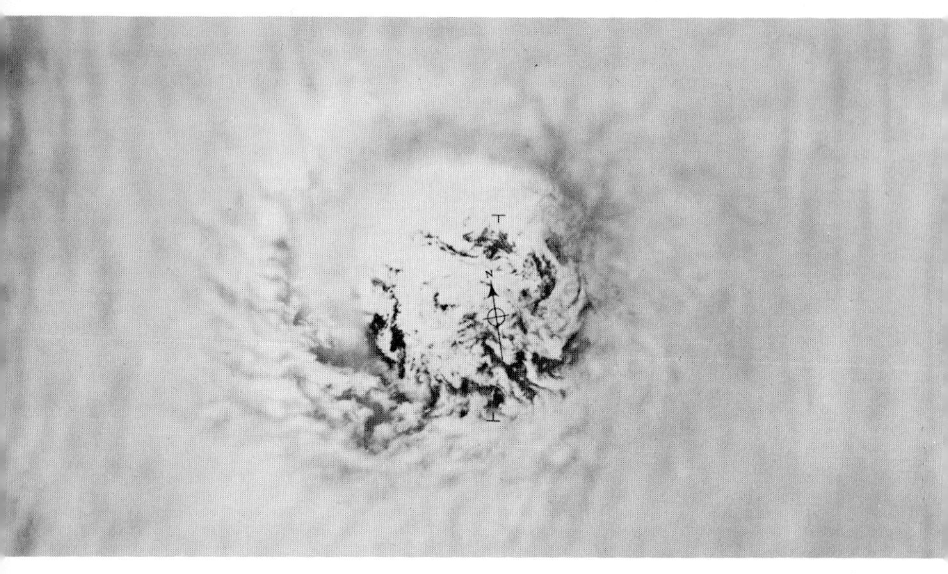

U.S. Air For

The eye of Hurricane Ida photographed from a U-2 plane of Project Stormfury. It hoped that someday these storms can be controlled by cooling them with silver iodi crystals.

U.S. Na

A Navy photographic plane flying above Hurricane Gracie.

Shell Oil Company

il refinery with adequate pollution controls, near Seattle. Oysters and mussels thrive
arby; the bay is full of smelt. Water discharged from the plant is so fresh that it must
pumped out to sea to avoid disturbing the salt-loving shellfish.

U.S. Army Corps of Engineers

gh water at Hickman, Kentucky, in 1912, before the days of effective flood control.

U.S. Army Corps of Engineers

(a) Tell City, Indiana, at the height of the 1937 flood.

U.S. Army Corps of Engine

(b) Tell City, Indiana, protected during 1945 flood.

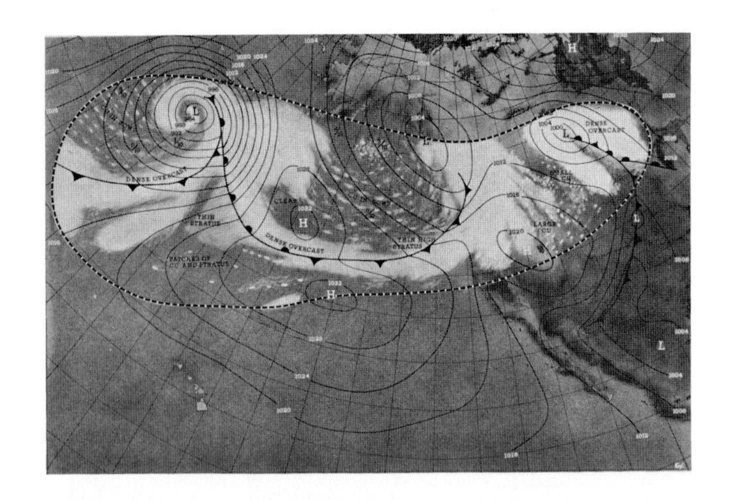

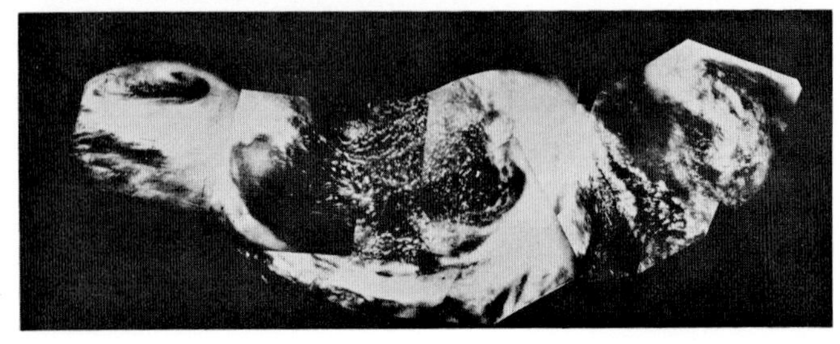

U.S. Department of Commerce, Weather Bureau

(top) Storm family over the North Pacific Ocean. Tiros cloud pictures superimposed conventional weather map.

(bottom) Actual Tiros cloud photographs (assembled in a mosaic) taken on May 20, 19

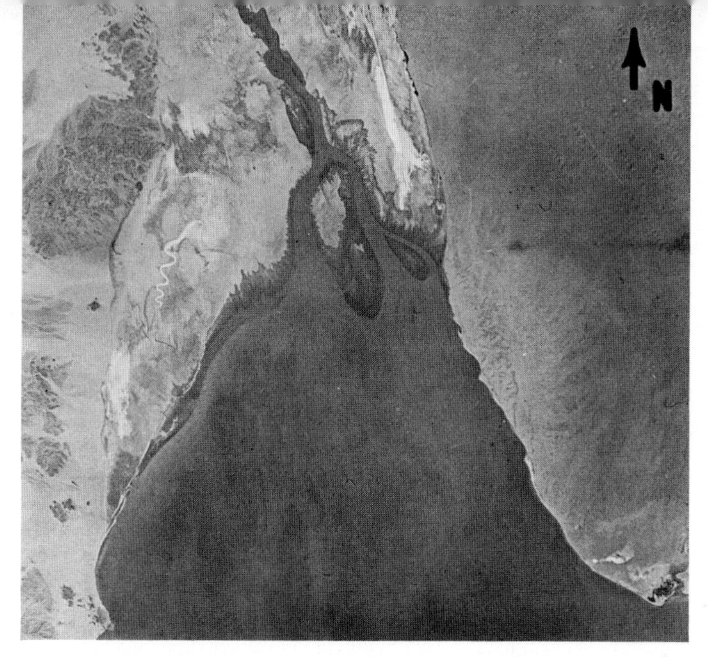

NASA

Delta of the Colorado River seen from above by Gemini 4 spacecraft. Such photos can be used to report changes in depth of shoals and even to spot forest fires.

U.S. Bureau of Reclamation

Glen Canyon Dam on the Colorado River. Beautiful Lake Powell, named for an early Army explorer of the gorge, slowly fills behind the dam, creating a large recreation area in the once-forbidding desert country.

U.S. Army Engine

Bonneville Dam on the Columbia River. The shoals at this point on the river of prevented steamboats from passing. Now ships pass easily through the locks, floodi is lessened, and water passing through the generators can produce 518,000 kilowatts electric power.

U.S. Department of Agricult

Strawberry plants in California are irrigated on flat land contours with slopes up to per cent. The water is shut off when the furrows are filled.

tion in the open sea needs to be increased to feed the world, how far can one go without going too far? It has been conservatively estimated that world production could be doubled; and some, with no basis whatsoever in fact, say that it could be increased ten or twelve times over. Studies of fish behavior and population on a world-wide basis must be made before it is too late.

Oceanography in the USSR

While there is international competition in the fishing industry, there has also been cooperation in international scientific work, one of whose functions is to serve fisheries. American oceanographers have been collaborating not only with those from Canada, Great Britain, western Europe, and South America, but also to a remarkable degree with the Russians.

The USSR has a very well-developed oceanographic program. Their showpiece is the 6000-ton *Lomonosov,* the world's largest ship built especially for marine research. It has sixteen distinct laboratories, and, unlike the less hospitable American components, a crew and scientific staff composed half of women. *Lomonosov* was named after a Russian scientist and historian whose *Brief Account of Travels in the Northern Seas,* published in 1763, laid the foundations for oceanography and meteorology in the Arctic. In that area, the ship that bears his name has found a gigantic undersea ridge running for 900 miles, close to the North Pole, across the Arctic from the Asiatic continental shelf to a spot near Ellesmere Island in northern Canada. The ridge towers from 6000 to 11,000 feet over the abyss. Cores taken from it show that the North Pole was once a center of volcanic activity.

During the Equalant expedition, *Lomonosov* worked with United States ships in the South Atlantic. It made a rendezvous with the Coast and Geodetic Survey's *Explorer* at a spot on the Equator midway between Africa and South America. The Soviets had planted a buoy for measuring sub-surface currents, but as a result of poor visibility had not been able to fix its position properly. The Americans stayed in the area, using the buoy as a reference point, while the Russians steamed east studying the current. When the skies cleared, the Americans got a good position and radioed the news to the Russians.

The Russians also have a smaller ship, the 2800-ton *Vityaz,* that was specially built for oceanography and has ranged widely about the world. In the Indian Ocean it discovered that several supposedly isolated sea-mounts were actually part of a submerged mountain chain that runs from the Bay of Bengal toward the Antarctic. They also discovered, north of New Zealand, a deep trench that is about 300 miles long and seems to reach a depth of 25,000 feet. On its thirty-fourth oceanographic cruise *Vityaz* found thirty new sea-mounts in the Pacific, two of which were named after the cosmonauts Yuri Gagarin and Gherman Titov. Free iron and manganese nodules were found in many places on the Pacific bottom, and like everyone else, the Russians wondered how they got there.

The *Vityaz* has figured in several instances of international cooperation. One of these occurred during a 1965 cruise in the Pacific, when the ship radioed Hawaii from Christmas Island, 1300 miles to the south, that a sailor aboard was critically ill with peritonitis. The Coast Guard flew a doctor and supply of blood for transfusions to Christmas Island, and brought the patient to a Honolulu hospital.

The following year the *Vityaz* pulled into Manila to take on fresh water, fruits, and vegetables, "and to get the laundry done." Short of funds, its captain asked the United States Embassy to send a wire to Moscow for help "because we consider the United States government a friend of Russia."

Reporting on a 1964 voyage of *Vityaz,* a Russian oceanographer wrote that "actual reserves of food in the ocean," in the form of the chemical raw material and algae, "exceeded the present possible consumption by millions of times. The coasts of many countries are lined with wide belts of algae. These waters could be used as feeding grounds for shellfish, fish, and plankton. The supply of living organisms in these feeding grounds can be greatly increased by artificial fertilization of sea water."

After a scientific visit to the USSR, Captain T. K. Treadwell of the U.S. Navy reported that "the Russians are obviously convinced that an understanding of the oceans can be made to pay off in substantially improved fish catches."

Captain Treadwell concluded that the Russian oceanographic effort was as great as any in the world. They are building new ships, graduating more scientists than the United States, and in general seem to be doing a good job. He was not very impressed, however, with the comfort of their shore facilities and he noticed they were making very little use of computers.

Impressed with the results of the Indian Ocean expedition, the Japanese have asked for a similar international venture in the North Pacific, to study the Kuroshio or Black Current—also called the Japan Current—which resembles the Gulf Stream in many ways. They enlisted the support of the USSR, which has a fishing fleet in the region warmed by the Current and would obviously be interested because of changes in its force and temperature in recent years that have made ships go much farther out to sea to make their catches.

The United States also agreed to participate, but then showed signs of backing out. Under the needling of economy-minded Congressmen, some government agencies have had doubts about the value of any more international efforts. Cooperating nations are supposed to send each other the records of data, and the Navy's oceanographic center is not getting all the results it expected. Nevertheless, in 1966 the United States did send representatives to an international conference in Moscow.

How Should the Federal Effort Be Organized?

Regardless of the enthusiasm of scientists, Congress has not made up its mind about the desirability of sharing information with any country that has ever sounded at all like a potential enemy. Congress has also had a hard time with the oceanographic effort in this country itself. Twenty-two different agencies of the federal government are involved in one way or another. The Interagency Committee on Oceanography, which has no budget and whose powers are merely advisory, includes representatives of the departments of Defense, Commerce, Interior, Health, Education and Welfare, Treasury, and State, as well as of the National Science Foundation, the Atomic Energy Commission, and the Smithsonian Institution. While most members of Congress believe in the value of the effort, if only because the United States must "keep up with the Russians," the whole matter is very untidy, and bills are frequently introduced to put it all under one roof as has been done with NASA, the space agency.

A step in this direction was taken with the combining of the Coast and Geodetic Survey and the Weather Bureau into the Environmental Science Services Administration. The old Survey, which had thirteen oceanographic ships in 1966, was founded by Thomas Jefferson in 1807 to help overcome the hazards of navigation at sea, and was the first scientific agency of the government. Its original job was merely to provide charts, but it has since acquired all sorts of others. It now provides aeronautical maps, check points for astronauts, surveys of Alaska, information for fishermen, and studies of the tides. One ship, *Explorer,* was assigned to spend all of 1965 in the Atlantic following the line of temperature (60° F.) that marks the edge of the Gulf Stream, so as to provide a better understanding of that meandering current. Probably the most dramatic of the survey's activities is the tsunami warning system in the Pacific. Tsunami is the Japanese word for the seismic, or "tidal," waves that roll across the wide ocean at high speeds after an earthquake. Tsunamis in the past have taken hundreds of lives and caused damage amounting to millions of dollars in low-lying parts of Hawaii and California. A wave originating from an earthquake in Alaska may reach Hawaii in a few hours. The function of the radio warning system is to get people away from the seashore before the waves, which may be fifty feet high, though they are not discernible from a ship at sea, reach the threatened area.

The work of the Weather Bureau hardly needs explanation. That the two agencies should be combined seemed logical, even to scientists. In the words of President Johnson, the ESSA is intended to provide "a single national focus for our efforts to describe, understand, and predict the state of the oceans, the state of the lower and upper atmosphere, and the size and shape of the earth."* Japan and the Soviet Union have already set up similar offices. Asked why the United States should be doing so just now, the new administrator, Dr. Robert White, replied, "The time just gets ripe. A number of trends began to come together."

The trends included new gadgets, such as sounding rockets, automatic buoys, computers, and satellites. Weather satellites show cloud patterns on a world-wide basis. Eventually they will also measure the temperature of the water's surface,

* Before a Congressional committee, Dr. Herbert Hollomon of the Department of Commerce added, "The creation of the ESSA is a response to the fact that the oceans, the upper and lower atmosphere, and the earth all interact and help determine each other—that the physical environment is a scientific whole and one aspect of the environment cannot be studied and understood in isolation."

and this information can be correlated with studies of currents made by the Coast and Geodetic Survey. The same satellites will also measure radiation from the sun and its effect on the atmosphere.

Research in the new agency will step up weather modification studies, and an integrated hazards-warning network will be established to alert the public to hurricanes, tornadoes, floods, earthquakes, and tsunamis.

If benefits can accrue from recognizing that the sea, the sky, and the land all interact, and from, accordingly, joining two agencies together to study them all, it may logically be asked why all the basic research about the sea now done by the Army, the Coast Guard, the National Science Foundation, the Smithsonian, and so on is not put under one roof. The answer is that all these human institutions like to perpetuate their own identities, and that, unlike the subject of space, which was so new that no department had any claims upon it, the nation's seas had been of concern to various departments of the government from the beginning. There is, moreover, remarkably little overlap on research projects: what the Department of the Interior, for instance, wants to know about the pollution of the sea has very little to do with what the Coast Guard and the Bureau of Commercial Fisheries want to know about the Labrador Current.

No matter how it is organized or reorganized by the federal government, the future of oceanography seems very bright. At present there is a great shortage of scientists—it is said that only 5000 people in the United States are at work in the field, and only about 500 are fully entitled to be known as oceanographers—so that anyone willing to learn his math can choose from among a number of grants that will provide him with work in a marine institution while he earns his graduate degree. Plenty of money is available from the federal government for research and more will be provided as soon as there are ships and scientists to use it.

Some industries appear somewhat disappointed that they have not made fortunes out of oceanography, as they have in the space race, but a number of corporations small and large are committed to it and will continue their efforts. Oceanography is a friendly profession, and its practitioners are dedicated. The nature of its difficulties these days is not primarily scientific.

The Future of Ocean Science

Two of the current problems of oceanography come under the heading of money. With the exception of fisheries research, the science of the sea received very little federal support until World War II. Centered at Woods Hole on the Atlantic and at Scripps on the Pacific, it was conducted by men seeking knowledge for its own sake. Woods Hole had one sailing ship and Scripps had only a few. Now all this is changed. There is money from the government, but the scientists are no longer their own masters.

New sea institutions opened up and there were scientific contracts for all of them from the government. The men in charge of appropriations in Washington have recognized the scorn of pure scientists for practical results, but they have also recognized that some kind of dividend must be shown to an inquisitive Congress.

An uneasy compromise has been worked out. Because of the shortage of trained oceanographers, a good deal of federal money is frankly spent on education. A considerable number of federal contracts go to pure research, in an acknowledgment that scientific results are unpredictable and that what seems completely abstract, as the structure of the atom once did, can suddenly turn out to have enormous material consequences. But though the government has become increasingly generous, the scientists still are not entirely happy.

For one thing, scientists almost by definition are not military-minded. They proceed by questioning, not by carrying out rules and regulations. They want to make constructive discoveries, rather than find new methods of destroying or avoiding destruction. Nevertheless, the scientists of the sea earn much of their living in the service of the United States Navy. A young seismologist at the Lamont Geological Laboratory is interested in earthquakes and how news of them is transmitted through the core of the earth, but he is aware that the trips he takes to various oceans, and the expensive equipment he places on the bottom of the sea, are paid for by men who want to know the same things for military reasons. They don't care about the seismicity of the earth, except as it may help in detecting enemy submarines. A chemist at Woods Hole was very much upset at being asked about the commercial value of the "funny water" he had investigated in the Red Sea, and he responded with a stern lecture on the impropriety of such a question. He also scorned the idea that the Indian Ocean expedition was designed to provide new food sources for the starving millions in Asia. That might be a result, he admitted, but it was not the sort of thing in which scientists are interested.

The other money problem for oceanographers has to do with the very unequal competition with space researchers for appropriations. In spite of the enormous physical potential of the sea, the sky gets about $5 billion annually from the federal government, while oceanography draws only several hundred million from the same source.

Those concerned with this disproportion often quote the statement by President Kennedy that "knowledge of the oceans is more than a matter of curiosity. Our very survival may hinge upon it." Mr. Kennedy was speaking not only of the nation's military needs, but of the vast amount of food that is grown and goes entirely to waste in the sea—food that, if we only knew how to harvest it efficiently, could support the multitudes who are going hungry today and may be a way of coping with the population explosion of the future. He was also talking about the vast reservoir of minerals and chemicals that are known to exist in the ocean, but which we do not yet know how to exploit at a reasonable cost. And he was thinking about the fresh water that might be extracted from it and of the possible benefits of knowing how to modify the weather.

When men start having such thoughts, they grow impatient. When they reflect that less than 1 per cent of the Navy's budget goes into oceanography, or that more money is spent putting one military officer into the realm of space than goes into a year's research in the fertile sea, they are inclined to become indignant. They would agree with Dean Athelstan Spilhaus of the University of Minnesota, who has said, "The ocean's bottom is at least as interesting as the moon's backside."*

In another vein, Dr. W. M. Chapman, a director of a West Coast seafood company, has written:

> If we devoted the same time and money to fixing up the food and welfare situation of that greater half of the world that still has to worry seriously about its daily bread, we could pretty well do it with not much more money and effort than we are spending on these shiny new toys. . . . There is almost nothing outlandish you can think of doing with, or in, or under the ocean that is not likely to prove to be very useful to us, and rather quickly.

There is one goal that would be just as difficult as putting a man on the moon, yet within the realm of possibilities. That goal would be the occupation of the deep-sea bed on behalf of the United States. You can't readily think of anything more prestigious or beneficial from the standpoint of the posture of the United States than to do this. The capability of occupying a piece

* It is interesting to note that 60 per cent of the moon's surface has been photographed and mapped while only 2 per cent of the bottom of the ocean has been properly charted.

of the deep sea bed would be so beneficial as to make the placement of colonies on Antarctica, or even on the moon, pale by comparison.

A lesser, but still enormous, prestigious, and useful goal, would be to put a man or two down on one of the higher spots of the Atlantic Ridge long enough to claim that spot as a piece of sovereign United States territory. That, even, would take a little shine off the moon adventure. A big advantage of this mid-goal is that if you could start at a depth of about 500 fathoms on this great adventure, you could work your way gradually downhill to the ultimate goal of occupying the deep sea floor. There will be found fabulous mineral riches beyond compare.

Dr. Chapman's dramatic approach to the sea might bring a cheer at a Chamber of Commerce luncheon or a meeting at the War College, but would have evoked less rapture in what is known as the "scientific community." The scientific men claim no interest in conquest, national glory, or enormous wealth. All they want to do is find out everything there is to know.

Living a thousand miles from the nearest ocean, Dean Spilhaus of the University of Minnesota was nevertheless moved to say, "The oceans offer us military, recreational, educational, economic, artistic, and intellectual outlets of unlimited space. Thus, they offer us more space than space itself in which to remain human. The sea . . . beautiful, elegant, strong, dangerous, and whimsical, challenges us."

7

The Watercourse of History

WATER has always had a part in shaping the history of mankind. It has brought prosperity and also plague. It has been both a highway and a barrier. Three times it saved England from conquest—from the Spanish Armada, from Napoleon, and from Hitler—but the English Channel was also, for the Romans, Angles, Saxons, and Normans, the avenue of conquest. Because of its island character, Japan managed to remain aloof from the West until Commodore Perry arrived by sea. Until 1492 the extent of the Atlantic kept Europe from suspecting that the Americas existed; but once the discovery had been made, the expanse did not prevent 50 million migrants from crossing. Australia remained aboriginal for two centuries more, but eventually not even the North Pole was safe from explorers by water.

The seas have always been a favored place for battles. From the days of the slave-powered trireme down to the present age of oil and atomic fuel, nations have regarded control of the sea as vital to their interests.

Water has always been no less vital to commerce. Even now, there is no easier or cheaper way to carry goods. Rivers such as the Rhine, the Seine, the Danube, and the Thames are great thoroughfares of trade, and in the uncharted lands of the New World such rivers as the Mississippi and the Amazon were indispensable for exploration and for bringing in settlers. Canals such as those of Suez and Panama have wiped out long sea routes, completely changing the assumptions of international affairs.

Water-caused Problems

The first great civilizations grew up along rivers—the Nile, the Huang Ho, the Indus, the Tigris-Euphrates. The Mesopotamian civilization finally succumbed to the same forces that had produced it. Along the low pressure belt of the 30° latitude, where it lies, is a strip which around the entire world has very little rainfall. The successive empires that flourished in the valley of the Tigris and the Euphrates solved this problem by irrigation. Unfortunately for them, they did not know how to keep the river bed from silting, so they had to build higher and higher banks to keep it on its course. When the levees finally reached a height of more than fifty feet, it became nearly impossible, even with slave labor, to build them any higher. The absolute dependence of these people on the river made them vulnerable to a peculiar kind of warfare: invaders several times diverted the rivers, leaving the defenders helpless. A further reason why the area today is desert is that the early civilizations knew no way to cleanse the land of the salt left behind by the evaporating irrigation water. Continued silting has now moved the delta and the mouth of the river two hundred miles out to sea from its location in ancient times.

The salting problem also vexed the Hohokam civilization that once existed in the area of what is now Phoenix, Arizona. This Indian culture lasted for 1400 years in that same arid 30° latitude with the help of irrigation from the Salt River. At one time a quarter of a million acres were under cultivation; but the deposits of salt finally destroyed their fertility, and today the only traces of the Hohokams are their abandoned canals.

The Mayan civilization was based on irrigation, and died when the land became so waterlogged that the roots of the corn plants drowned. Clearly, the Mayans understood nothing about drainage.

The Romans managed to make the Egyptian desert bloom for a time by tapping the ground water in artesian wells. The water was not replenished, however, and the supply eventually ran out. In their own capital city the Romans established a magnificent system of aqueducts. They also built a prodigious sewer, the Cloaca Maxima, which discharged all the wastes of the metropolis into the rich farm land of the Campagna. In time this became a great swamp, a breeding place for typhoid and malaria, and one theory has it that the Roman Empire fell because the citizens were so weakened by these diseases that they were unable to defend themselves.

With one exception, all the great cities of the world have grown up on navigable bodies of water. They used to be ravaged quite regularly by the water-borne disease of cholera. In 1841 the life expectancy in Liverpool and Manchester was twenty-six years, and it wasn't a great deal better in other metropolises. Then the relation between contaminated water and disease became understood.

Today few city doctors in the United States would recognize a case of cholera if they saw it. In Egypt, however, an epidemic of cholera occurs about every eleven years, and in Calcutta, the largest city in India, with an indifferent water supply and very poor sanitation, the disease is endemic.

Certainly Indian government officials know the cause, but apparently they are helpless in the face of poverty and overpopulation.

Some developing nations do not yet seem to have learned the lesson of water in cities. The World Bank advised officials of the Nigerian city of Lagos to build a sewer system. The local government listened to other advisers instead, and used force to clear a seventy-acre slum for building of skyscrapers. They ran out of money before the buildings were completed; now 85 per cent of the schoolchildren have hookworm and 10 per cent of the city's deaths are caused by diarrhea or dysentery.

Mistakes about water can have all sorts of dire consequences. A French Army officer who liked the strategic location founded New Orleans in a spot that was obviously too low and subject to flooding by the Mississippi River. Since then the dead have had to be buried above ground, and as recently as 1965 a hurricane-caused flood pushed the river through a good portion of the city.

People have frequently built high dams in mountainous regions and then built towns in the narrow valleys underneath them. In recent years such dams have burst in Italy and in southern France, and in the last century one above Johnstown, Pennsylvania, gave way, taking thousands of lives as the water poured through the town.

In spite of repeated experience, people continue to build on flood plains, such as the valley of the Minnesota River, where it is quite demonstrable that sooner or later the rivers that built those plains will return to claim the land. Likewise, people also build houses on dunes by the ocean, where winter storms or hurricanes are certain eventually to wash them away. That is what happened at Fire Island, New York, in March 1963, when a very high tide coincided with a very strong wind that blew steadily from the east for three days. The ocean became like a river in spring flood as it poured in parallel to the beach and cut away the dunes. Houses built at the top of the dunes, with no regard to the laws of nature, were toppled onto the beach, and many disappeared into the sea without a trace.

The United States and the United Nations probably should have been wise enough not to invest millions of dollars in a dam in the Artibonite Valley of the tragic country of Haiti. To prevent silting, thousands of trees were planted on the steep hills around the dam; but who could hope to keep the peasants from cutting down every tree for the fuel they desperately need for cooking? They neither understood nor cared that in so doing they caused the dam to fill up with mud, and to become useless even before it was finished.

It is hard to say just what kind of mistake was made about water in Mexico City, or how it could have been avoided. The city is built on a dried lake bed, with a vast and porous aquiter underneath. For centuries the city has drawn its water from this source, restoring none of it, and pouring its sewage down over the mountains miles away. As skyscrapers were built, and the city became one of the largest in the hemisphere, it began to sink. The center of town is still sinking, and with each new suburb that is added it drops another inch or so.

One of the most colossal mistakes ever made about water shows up on the map as a big blue lake at the southern end of California. Settlers in the hot and dry but fertile Imperial Valley, just north of Mexico and just south of Death Valley, saw the Colorado River as the answer to their water problems. In 1901 an irrigation canal from the Colorado was completed that followed the course of the dry Alamo River, one of the Colorado's overflow channels.

The Colorado usually flooded in the later spring and early summer, when the snows melted in the mountains. There were also occasional flash floods from tributaries. The river in flood carried enormous amounts of sediment, which clogged the new irrigation canals, and in 1904 the spring flood left the upper four miles of the Imperial Canal badly clogged with silt. At this spot the land has an elevation of one hundred feet above sea level. The Salton Sink, at the bottom of the valley, is 280 feet *below* sea level.

In the autumn of 1904, when the danger of flood was thought to be months away, a bypass was built to avoid the silted four miles of the canal. There was no gate to regulate the flow. By March 1905 three unusual floods had occurred on the river. Dams built to close the bypass came too late and a fourth and fifth flood washed them away.

The Colorado deepened the canal, found the bed of the Alamo River, and began flowing down into the Salton Sink. For sixteen months, until November 1906, it ran untamed along this course, ruining farms, destroying houses, railways, and highways, and threatening lives. The Salton Sea, as it is now called, remains today as the consequence of a serious and costly mistake.

The Positive Side

While it is instructive to talk about people's mistakes, they are, of course, only part of the story of water and of history. Mankind has learned most of its lessons very well. In the so-called developed countries, water-borne epidemics have been eliminated. In the United States sufficient water has been found, for the present at least, to produce agricultural surpluses and to process a constantly expanding economy.

Falling water is used as a basic source of energy in the form of hydroelectric plants. As steam, it ran the railroads that settled the American West, and for a time it even ran an automobile, known as the Stanley Steamer. In New Zealand and Italy, steam from natural geysers is used today to run power plants.

In medicine, water has been used to reduce fever, calm the mentally disturbed, sterilize instruments, rehabilitate the crippled muscles of polio victims, and to treat all sorts of ailments in spas and thermal baths. The governess of deaf, dumb, and blind Helen Keller finally reached her charge's darkened consciousness by holding the girl's hand under the faucet and spelling out the word "water" on her palm.

The human race in its ingenuity in dealing with water has produced many beautiful objects—birch-bark canoes, the graceful boats of the Polynesians, clipper ships, great ocean liners, sleek speedboats, soaring dams and bridges. Windmills to pump water have accidentally added charm to the flat landscapes of Holland and the prairies of the United States.

While it is obvious that there could be no agriculture without water for the crops, it is not quite so well recognized that without water there would not even be any soil to grow things. Literally, we eat rocks; there is basically nothing else to eat. What we call earth is nothing but rocks that have been ground into minute particles by the timeless action of raindrops. The earth, of course, is enriched by decaying bits of organic matter, but the initial creation of soil on our planet was all the work of moving water.

Soil, of course, was necessary to produce the vegetation that nourishes land animals and therefore was basic to the evolution that finally led to man. This same evolution produced types of life that require a very specialized combination of soil and water, the swamps and marshes that are the natural homes of waterfowl. Man, in his anxiety to develop everything in sight, now threatens this particular kind of habitat with schemes to drain wetlands and turn them into farms. Fortunately for the less ingenious members of creation, there are a number of people who make it their concern that at least part of our watery environment be preserved for the animals with whom we share the earth.

Among the infinite ways water affects us is its influence on our moods. Rain, gloomy weather, and thunderstorms have always been poetically supposed to affect human behavior, and now there are statistics from the World Meteorological Organization to sustain the belief. During a storm, births rise by 11 per cent, deaths by 20 per cent, pain increases in the chronically ill, polio admissions to hospitals rise by 6 per cent and mining accidents by 12 per cent. Human reactions in general are said to be 6 per cent slower on stormy days.

Water is also a source of pleasure in many ways. After the beauty of nature, in the romantic nineteenth century, began to be recognized rather than avoided, the beauty of water could be seen in such varied forms as the wild ocean, the blue calm of a lake like Coeur d'Alene, the glaciers of Switzerland, and such scenes began to be painted. Water had earlier been used ornamentally in formal pools (Has the Taj Mahal ever been photographed without its accompanying pool?) and in the great fountains of Rome and of the Mohammedans. Sensually it was valued in the famous baths of Rome and of Turkey, and soap is advertised today with pictures of happy people standing under showers of running water. For pleasure, too, the popularity of all sorts of water sports keeps increasing in activities such as swimming, fishing, all sorts of boating, surfing, and water skiing.

Water has also had mystical meanings down through the ages, and in baptism it is used to wash away sins. To Hindus a whole river, the Ganges, is sacred. One could also suggest that there is almost something mystical about the fact that American astronauts land on water, rather than earth, when they crash back onto the planet.

It is truly an amazing fluid. And one of the less recognized, amazing things about water is its role in the prosperity of the United States.

8

The Water Cost of Prosperity

IT is "the overwhelming paradox of the nation's prosperity," Secretary of the Interior Stewart Udall said in 1965, "that the quality of the American environment has declined with each new advance in the economic indices. Pollution and blight have emerged not from poverty but from prosperity. Our factories pour out more products—and our rivers carry the heaviest pollution." In his first State of the Union message, President Kennedy pointed out that "every river system in America is now polluted."

When Henry Hudson first saw the river that now bears his name, he described it as a noble stream with abundant fish, surrounded by fine lands with plenty of clear water. When Senator Robert F. Kennedy visited the shore of the Hudson near Nyack, New York, in 1965 he saw old auto parts, oil drums, garbage, empty beer cans, green scum on the rocks. A bottle dipped into the river brought out water that was brown and opaque. When asked how it appeared to him, he replied, "Dirty."

Some of this pollution, of course, is municipal waste, but much of it comes from the leather factories, the meat and chicken processors, the assembly plants, the breweries, and the oil barges that use the river. The shad runs in the spring on the Hudson used to bring tons of the delicate fish to New York City tables. Now few are caught and fewer still are edible. In 1964 two little girls contracted typhoid fever after eating a watermelon they had dredged from a branch of the river.

Salmon fishing in Maine is no longer much of a sport now that such rivers as the Androscoggin, the Penobscot, and the Kennebec are so often full of tan, foamy pulp from the bustling paper mills. The Connecticut River has been called "the world's most beautifully landscaped cesspool." Industrial residues have poured into it in such a degree that swimming, considered unwise for the last fifty years, has now become absolute folly.

The shellfish beds of Narragansett Bay are being studied by the University of Rhode Island to see if there is any way to save them from the polluted water. At Blue Point, Long Island, their once famous home, oysters are no longer safe to eat. The waters there have been poisoned by runoff from duck farms.

Little boys are rarely seen swimming on the Delaware River, now that the industrial complex runs all the way from Trenton, New Jersey, to below Wilmington, Delaware.

The Potomac, once heavily polluted at times of low water, has been taken in hand by the Public Health Service, which says it is now safe though heavily silted. The Army Engineers calculate that it will take ten years to remove the accumulation of sludge from the river bottom.

Is Lake Erie Dead?

In April 1965 the Public Health Service began a series of hearings on the condition of Lake Erie, a great sea highway in an area of great industries, and a body of water that must supply the domestic needs of millions of people. Commercial fishing hardly exists on the lake. One by one, beaches along the shore have had to be closed, and boating has declined because of the filth that gathers on hulls. Erie tapwater has an unpleasant taste and odor. Mayflies, once a summer spectacle during their one-day breeding season, disappeared from the region some time ago. These insects spend their entire lives as grubs in the bottom of the lake, except for the one day of their existence when they all emerge at once for their mating flight. The males all die immediately after mating, and the females die as soon as they have dropped their fertilized eggs onto the water. Though to some residents of towns along Lake Erie the mayflies may have been only a nuisance, the fish in the lake lost an important source of food, and another natural wonder has been destroyed.

Erie is an aging lake, one that in time will have gradually filled up with plant life, and that after thousands of years will have become dry land. The process of deterioration has been spectacularly hastened, however, by the enormous amounts of nitrogen and phosphate fertilizers that are washed off the farms and that encourage exuberant breeding of plant life in the water. The plants deplete the oxygen needed to decompose wastes, and fish such as trout, perch, and whitefish are displaced by less desirable species such as buffalofish and carp. As Senator Gaylord Nelson of Wisconsin has said, "Lake Erie is no longer simply water. It is a chemical tank." A Public Health Service report on the Detroit area of Lake Erie said that 1.6 billion gallons of filthy industrial and municipal water were being poured out every day, and that each day the lake received some seven million pounds of alien chemicals.

Of the nineteen booming industries in the area, which were told three years ago that they must do something about their polluting activities, only ten have actually taken remedial measures. It is reported that the anti-pollution laws of Michigan are enforced much more strictly in outlying parts of the state than around Detroit, where according to the *New York Times,* "the concentration of multibillion dollar industries exerts pronounced influence on public affairs."

The Ford Motor Company, whose wastes by volume are said to contribute most of the industrial effluent poured into the Raisin and Rouge rivers, which later flow into Lake Erie, issued a five-page report outlining all the steps taken by the company. A highly technical paper, it nowhere made mention of a time when the polluting practices might be stopped.

In 1965 further hearings on Lake Erie were held by the Public Health Service in Cleveland and Buffalo. (The Erie basin includes parts of Michigan, Ohio, Pennsylvania, New York, and Canada, and polluted rivers from Indiana also run into it.) At Buffalo, Murray Stein, an enforcement officer for the Service, remarked that the pollution he had just observed at Niagara Falls left him "not proud that I am an American."

The hearings in Buffalo were enlivened by one of those states' rights controversies that serve only to cloud the already muddy waters. Governor Rockefeller of New York declared that his state's contribution to the destruction of Lake Erie was not an interstate matter, that the water flowed east, and that therefore the Public Health Service had nothing to say about what New York did. (Nevertheless, the Governor wants the federal government to give him $600 million for statewide pollution control, so long as Washington has as little as possible to say about how it is spent.)

At the end of the hearings the Governor did at least agree, along with the other states involved, to a four-year program for cleaning up the lake. Whether the lake is truly dying is not yet clear. It is certainly sick. At best, according to the *New York Times,* "Lake Erie's convalescence will take many years."

What the Public Health Service Did

Lake Michigan is in almost as bad condition as Lake Erie. The columnist Drew Pearson wrote that it "is turning into a cesspool. A study of the pollution of the lake bottom shows that the situation is practically irreversible." Michigan has been called the "killer lake" because of the thousands of wildfowl that now die mysteriously on its shores. Chicago draws a great deal of drinking water from the lake, while the steel mills a few miles to the south pour metallic acid and oil wastes into it. The Public Health Service held a hearing on this as well, and received full cooperation from all the industries. They agreed to accept responsibility for the condition of the lake, and a table of abatement measures was drawn up.

Although criticized by many for not doing enough, the Public Health Service of the United States Department of Health, Education and Welfare took a number of enforcement actions under the Water Pollution Control Act of 1948. These actions have involved some very large corporations, as well as a thousand municipalities. The pollution of more than 7000 miles of streams was reduced, and more than a billion and three-quarter million dollars worth of treatment facilities were built.

The Public Health Service took action concerning the sulphuric acid that drains from abandoned coal mines in Appalachia and concerning the meat packers in the towns of St. Joseph, Omaha, Kansas City, and Sioux City on the Missouri—only the town of St. Joseph, by refusing to comply voluntarily, obliged the Service to go to court. It also acted against the operators of oil wells in Arkansas that were seeping oil and salt water, and of uranium mines in Colorado that were discharging radioactive water, as well as against a number of food processors in Idaho, Wyoming, and Utah who were found to be polluting the water supply. There have been numerous similar actions on interstate rivers in both East and West.

An action taken on the Mississippi River has all the elements of a mystery story with the title of "Who Killed the Catfish?" The one point of agreement among those involved is that since 1958 something like 50 million fish have died in the river, most of them in the course that passes through Louisiana. The sudden death of five million fish at a single stroke brought the Public Health Service in to investigate.

On March 19, 1964, the Public Health Service and the State of Louisiana jointly announced to the newspapers that five different teams of investigators, working separately over a period of some months, had determined that the deaths were caused by two unidentified substances and by two known pesticides, endrin and dieldrin.

On April 3, 1964, the Public Health Service reported that with new and sophisticated research techniques they had found endrin in dead fish in quantities of one-fortieth of a part in a million, and that this minute quantity had been lethal. It was further said that there were only two firms in the United States that manufactured endrin—Shell Chemical of Denver, whose management promised complete cooperation in the investigation, and the Velsicol Company of Chicago, whose endrin plant was in Memphis, at a factory six miles away from the river.

Four days later the *New York Times* reported Dr. Leon Weinberger of the Public Health Service as saying he had "positive evidence" of the part played by endrin. The same news story quoted Dr. Bernard Lorant, head of research at Velsicol: "All circumstances show there is no significant environmental contamination with endrin." Dr. Lorant went on to suggest the deaths might be caused by "invisible factors," including the intrusion of salt water from the Gulf of Mexico.

A news release on April 23, 1964, reported that the discharge of endrin had been going on for years, and that the chemical had soaked into the mud, where it killed fish that were bottom feeders. The release added that routine water purification did not remove endrin, and that the New Orleans supply of drinking water came from the river. Wastes from Velsicol, it was reported, had been dumped into Cypress Creek and Wolf River, which drain into the Mississippi. Water samples showed gross contamination.

Dr. Lorant, reached by phone at Baton Rouge, denied that Velsicol was responsible for the fish deaths, and that Public Health Service officials had been denied entry to the plant. He added that the symptoms of fish deaths were not like those of endrin poisoning, and that the Louisiana Fish and Wildlife Commission agreed with him. He challenged the validity of the experimental method used and said that the conclusions were unsound.

Louisiana authorities said they had put fish in water containing endrin in quantities of nine to ten parts to a million, and that the fish were still living after three days. They said also that they had repeated a Public Health test of injecting material from dying fish into mice, and that the mice had lived. What the newspapers did not report was that Don Mount, a young biologist at the Public Health Service's Taft Center in Cincinnati, had carried out a series of elimination tests on fish, ruling out metallic wastes, disease, and so on, until all that was left to cause the deaths were chlorinated hydrocarbons such as endrin. After testing endrin on fish, he concluded that the dead fish found in the river contained more than enough to kill them. The Public Health Service felt sure that it had a case. It is of interest to note that Don

"endrin is an important insecticide to the $325-million cotton industry in the Yazoo Delta." He respectfully requested, therefore, that there be no restrictions on the use of endrin until it was shown that correct agricultural use of it was contributing to the contamination of the river. Dr. D. E. Ferguson said he had not studied fish from the Mississippi or the species reported killed, but that many kinds of fish were able to tolerate very high concentrations of pesticide. The testimony of R. A. Lafleur implicated endrin in fish deaths in Louisiana, some involving 100,000 pounds of fish in a single kill. Since the river was leveed in his state, he reasoned, there could be no runoff of the pesticide from its farms; therefore the runoff must have come from upriver. Should the source of contamination prove to be a manufacturing plant upstream, he asked for federal action "to cause the cessation of such discharge to the end that Louisiana's Mississippi River will not be contaminated." Another Louisianan, L. S. St. Amant, testified that the commercial fish industry of the state ranged up to $100 million a year, employing 50,000 people, and that whether or not endrin was killing fish, it would be unrealistic to assume that insecticides can be continuously added to the water year after year without expecting disastrous effects sooner or later. He added that probably the only reason shrimp kills had not yet been seen was because shrimp live and die on the bottom. L. D. Newsom of Louisiana retorted that new machines and chemicals were often dangerous, and that if the number of deaths and injuries caused by automobiles had been known at the beginning of the century, they probably would have been outlawed. "As for detrimental effects on wildlife species," he went on, "the plow and the saw have been by far the most disruptive tools ever invented by man." He did not advocate the outlawing of pesticides. Neither did anyone else at the hearing. Other speakers cited the population explosion and the value of the sugar crop.

In the official release following this conference, the representatives of Louisiana and Mississippi were reported to have agreed that endrin was the cause of the fish kill, and those from Arkansas that it probably contributed, whereas those from Tennessee believed other factors might be involved.

The day after the conference, the Public Health Service announced from Washington, that endrin had been killing millions of fish for four years. The Service had begun by saying that this was "most likely"; now it stated flatly that endrin was responsible. At first it had been believed that the source was the agricultural runoff of pesticides, and it was still believed there must be other sources than Velsicol, since the amount of endrin in the river was two or three times greater at New Orleans than at Memphis. The announcement suggested that a possible source might be the firms that packaged endrin under various brand names, or the waste water from sugar cane mills. The release concluded by expressing concern over the possible fate of a million human water consumers.

Congressman Jamie L. Whitten of Mississippi called the report one-sided, and protested, "In this instance it is not claimed that health is affected."

On June 17 Senator Dirksen of Illinois, whose constituents include the Velsicol Company of Chicago, demanded that the Public Health Service be investigated. They had, he said, made "wild accusations" and had "unjustly crucified" a manufacturer before they had all the facts. The Senator called it "ridiculous" that endrin should travel 700 miles before killing, and concluded, "Some have become so intoxicated with power that our federal government now need not be held responsible for its wild charges."

On June 27 the Secretary of the Department of Health, Education and Welfare said that the verdict on endrin was official. Officers of Velsicol expressed "amazement that Secretary Celebrezze would accept such a report, since the conclusions drawn at the New Orleans conference are not supported by the scientific evidence offered there."

On July 10, 1964, the Public Health Service released a report from Louisiana that there had been fish kills in five bayous and canals in the single week of June 29 to July 6. The water in these bayous and canals has no direct connection at all with the Mississippi.

At a Senate committee hearing on July 29, 1964, Dr. Lorant of Velsicol accused Murray Stein of conducting a "kangaroo court" in New Orleans, and denied that endrin was responsible for the death of 51 million fish. He added that most of the fish killed were menhaden, a salt-water fish, and that the Public Health Service had no evidence as to the cause of death, having taken only three blood samples from fish—a quantity "grossly insufficient to support any conclusions."

Senator Ribicoff, at the hearing, called Velsicol a "long-distance killer" and said the company had disposed of endrin waste in a "primitive and dangerous manner." Addressing the company representative, he added, "The record is overwhelmingly against your position. I think the evidence indicates you are wrong." The Senator also wondered out loud "how Memphis lets you get away with it!"

On January 17, 1965, George Putnicki of the Public Health Service reported having found 8000 pounds of endrin in a sewer near the Velsicol plant. He said it would "create an enormous health hazard if it reached the Mississippi."

When this story broke, two older stories about Velsicol were also suddenly revealed. On January 30, 1963, the Memphis Health Department had received complaints from twenty persons who lived near Cypress Creek, whose water Velsicol uses as a coolant. The complaints mentioned nausea, vomiting, and watery eyes, apparently as a result of gas in the stream. Wilson Keyes, Velsicol's director of manufacturing, asserted that "endrin could not have caused the symptoms." On June 7 of the same year, twenty-six workmen from factories near Velsicol were taken to the hospital suffering from chlorine fumes. (Endrin is a chlorinated hydrocarbon.) Damage suits adding up to $5 million were filed against the company.

Shortly thereafter, Velsicol had given a dinner for 150 political, civic, and business leaders. "It came as quite a shock to us," John Kirk, president of the company, told the guests, "to discover that there was some question about whether we were welcome in the city of Memphis."

Mayor Henry Leeb, speaking in reply, assured him, "This plant is very much wanted by Memphis."

The Memphis sewer in which endrin had been found was sealed off until it could be cleaned out—an operation the Velsicol Company paid for.

Months later Dr. Lorant was still positive that the case against endrin had not been proved. He pointed out that most of the fish kills were seasonal, occurring in October and November—months when pesticides were not being applied to crops. The seasonal aspect, in his opinion, also ruled out the theory of accidental spillage from the factory. Why should accidents occur only in those two months? He remarked again on the fact that only three dead fish had been tested in a laboratory, and that these had been taken from the river 700 miles away from the Velsicol plant. No fish kills occurred in the Mississippi in 1965.

On balance, it would seem that the Public Health Service, which had been doing an excellent job all over the United States, may have shown too much zeal in the effort to find someone guilty in this case, and that the mystery of "Who Killed the Catfish?" has still not been satisfactorily solved.

What is Pollution?

The definition of the word "pollute" is "to make or render unclean, to defile, desecrate, profane." The definition is important in the controversial case of the Mahoning River, a small tributary of the Ohio River that flows eastward from Ohio into Pennsylvania, thus making it an interstate stream. The American steel industry started on the Mahoning, and there are many large plants along it. The steel industry in the valley, and all the employment it provides, are utterly dependent on the river, whose water is used to cool molten steel. The Public Health Service said the river is polluted. The steel industries disputed the point and added that if they are forced to make costly changes in their mode of operation they will be forced to close down.

Much dramatic use has been made in the controversy of the fact that the temperature of the Mahoning water was once recorded at 117° F. (Since then conditions have improved to the extent that temperatures rarely exceed 100°.) Its appearance was described as follows by the Public Health Service: "Oil and grease coat its surface and discolor its banks, suspended solids destroy its clarity, sludge covers its beds, and oil clings to tree limbs and bushes." There are no fish in it, nor any other from of aquatic life. Acid, lime, oil, and grease from the steel plants have forced its abandonment as water for municipal use, hindered its use by other industries, and absolutely destroyed it for recreation.

The Mahoning area, which includes the city of Youngstown, has a population of about half a million people, and produces about 7 per cent of all the steel manufactured in the United States. The river does not endanger the health of the population, because they draw their water from outside reservoirs. Pollution, as a public health matter, is proved downstream at Beaver Falls, Pennsylvania, town of 65,000 which has to use more chlorine than almost any water system in the country to make the supply safe. But Beaver Falls has made no official complaint.

The steel mills are outmoded, and their owners are angered by the federal government's interference. Three of the mills refused to give federal agents any information about their production. Congressman Michael Kirwan, representing the district, says, "The Mahoning is an industrial river and always has been. It is for people, not for fish. There's plenty of fishing in streams nearby." Although they deny any wrongdoing, the mills are now taking steps to reduce the amounts of chemicals and minerals they put into the river, and all sewage from the factories is to be treated.

The Mahoning River situation raises some important questions. What is a river for? What, precisely, is pollution? Must water endanger human health before it can be declared polluted? Do the steel companies have the right to make a profit by destroying a river that belongs to all the people? Is the economic well-being of 500,000 people who are dependent on the steel plants more important than the welfare of the 65,000 people of Beaver Falls? Pollution becomes such a problem because it is so intricately caught up in all the various and conflicting goals sought by the American public.

The answer to the question "What is pollution?" involves millions of dollars. If a river is not used for drinking water, and fish are not expected to live in it, then the unsightly Mahoning is not polluted, according to the steel manufacturers, so long as human health is not at stake. Therefore, they argue, the costly job of cleaning up the Mahoning is unnecessary.

How much are you willing to spend to make your river fit for brook trout? Or, as was asked on the East Coast, why spend $12 million to save a $1 million shellfish industry? If money is the only standard by which the United States is to live, then all that needs to be done about polluted water is to add enough chlorine to make it safe to drink. Fortunately for those who deplore it, pollution turns out to be quite expensive. Rivers and lakes that might have been used for recreation—which can bring a good deal of money to an area—mean the loss of considerable revenue if they are unfit for use. An area with polluted water will hardly attract any new industry dependent on water, or one needing new workers who might understandably be reluctant to move to a community with so little self-respect. It is unrealistic to argue that pollution control costs too much. Not controlling it eventually costs even more. Federal officials now state that keeping the water clean must be reckoned as part of the cost of doing business, and in the long run this attitude is likely to prevail.

In contrast to the philosophy of the water-users on the Mahoning River are the sponsors of the Wild Rivers Bill, who would set aside parts of the Salmon, Clearwater, Rogue, Rio Grande, and Eleven Point rivers from any abuse by man at all. Also in contrast was the statement of James M. Quigley of the Public Health Service:

> There are still some who hold to the belief that the utilization of a stream as a receptacle of waste is a legitimate use of water. . . . Such a belief finds its basis in the fact that watercourses have been used for this purpose all the way back to antiquity. Whatever may have been unacceptable or unavoidable in years past, however, it is clear that our goal now and in the years ahead, in an age of vast industrial expansion and rapid urbanization, must be to prevent *any* sort of pollution.

Somewhere in between lies the statement of the late President Herbert Hoover, an ardent fisherman, whose opinion is endorsed by many industrial leaders:

> After all we are an industrial people. We have to work eight hours a day and all but a few weeks in the year, and we cannot

abolish our industries and still pay for fishing tackle. So I have long since come to the conclusion that what we need is a division of streams into three categories.

Mr. Hoover went on to make three recommendations: streams that had never been polluted should be forever free from industry in the future; streams that are absolutely ruined should be left that way because of the crushing cost of trying to bring them back to an acceptable condition; and streams that can be saved at a reasonable cost should gradually be brought back to a state of purity.

What is decided about pollution and who sets the water standards are obviously bread-and-butter questions. The Public Health Service, which had considerable power but felt that it should have more, asked Congress for the final say on how pure water ought to be. A bill to this effect was introduced by Senator Muskie of Maine, and brought out a rash of objections from those industries that did not want to be controlled by any ardent young "clean stream" boys from Washington.

The Chamber of Commerce made a statement that "there should be adequate federal authority in the background" but that "in all public activities with respect to pollution control there should be full opportunity for local, municipal, and industrial representation." The National Association of Manufacturers declared:

State and local responsibility in this area should not be weakened through federal subsidies and federal enforcement actions. Federal regulation is particularly ill-fitted in this field since every water problem is different. Blanket requirements issued on a national basis would be highly unrealistic and result in unjustified economic costs, both in terms of job opportunities and in terms of this country's competitive position in world markets.

In other words, let's not do anything about pollution if it's going to cost anybody money.

Almost simultaneously the White House Conference on Natural Beauty went on record as saying, "The historic American overemphasis on economic costs and benefits in building water control structures should be reversed. We must insist on beauty as one of the essential elements in water-related planning."

A tough bill giving the Public Health Service complete power to set pure water standards passed the Senate, then bogged down in committee in the House of Representatives, which is traditionally more responsive to lobbyists. There it was opposed by spokesmen for chemical plants, paper mills, and steel mills, some of the nation's largest users of water. Bethlehem Steel proposed that Public Health Service decisions be subject to judicial review—which would make it possible to tie things up in courts for years while the companies went ahead with business as usual. A compromise bill signed in 1965 gives cities and industries the right to appeal specifications once they are established. The bill also increased the amount of federal money available to help communities build treatment plants.

In signing the bill President Johnson said that "additional, bolder legislation will be needed in the years ahead. The clear, fresh waters that were our national heritage have become dumping grounds for garbage and filth. No river should run red with the blood from slaughterhouses." The federal government will continue to press for more power, in the belief that since so many communities are laggard themselves about doing anything to stop pollution, they cannot be expected to press powerful local industries very hard. In 1966 federal enforcement of anti-pollution laws was transferred to the Department of the Interior, with the thought that it would proceed more vigorously and over a wider spectrum than was possible for the medically-minded Public Health Service.

Among other ways that have been suggested for getting industry to do something about pollution, one has been to offer tax incentives for putting new pollution-abating equipment in factories. This does not appeal very much to towns that receive a good part of their income from taxes on business property, or to the United States Treasury, which fears that it would lose too much revenue. Another proposal has been to follow the example of the Ruhr Valley in Germany, where steel producers are charged for the cost of all the cleaning up made necessary by their polluting activities. This idea has brought cries of anguish in the United States, but appears to be working very well on the Ruhr.

The Solvay Story

Industry is, of course, not composed entirely of "bad guys" intent on destroying our streams and lakes. Sometimes they are innocent victims, used by cities to cover up their own unwillingness to spend money on sewage systems. Such was the plight of the Solvay Process plant on Lake Onondaga at Syracuse. This plant uses the only two mineral resources the area has to offer in manufacturing soda ash, a product used in hundreds of industries. People driving by the Solvay plant on the lake held their noses. The place smelled, and of course Solvay was accused of polluting it.

In fact, Lake Onondaga's water never had been good for drinking. The Indians avoided it, even though fish found it quite habitable. For years, the city of Syracuse poured in raw sewage and no one complained, except about Solvay. Then, when the lake began to be septic, Solvay offered the city a chance to pump sewage through its own chemical waste beds. There the solids were chemically destroyed, and the water ran clean and sterile into the lake. The worst of the smell went away.

When some time later Solvay had to look for new waste beds, and found them much farther away, Syracuse was faced with the task of building its own sewage disposal facilities. It took four years to put up the money. Meanwhile the problem was solved by burying part of the sewage along the south side of the lake and pouring the rest straight into it. The lake became "visibly polluted," and Solvay again got the blame. At the height of these undeserved attacks, the company decided to give up and close down the factory. The thought of losing its largest industry alarmed the city, and the disposal plant was rushed to completion.

Because its operations are so large and so visible, industry is often singled out as the major offender in pollution—a belief that is fostered, consciously or unconsciously, by those unwilling to face the cost of doing their own part to solve the problem. The industrial contribution to it is certainly large, since so much water is needed for almost all kinds of manufacture, but the majority of firms are not heedless of their responsibility and are doing a great deal to control their operations. A national committee on industrial wastes, formed in 1950, has been active principally in trying to solve the enormous technical problems caused by the bewilderingly varied ways in which water is used. Most industries need good water as a matter of self-interest, and it is a good deal cheaper in the industrial process to use water that needs no treatment first.

The Role of the Oil Business

The oil industry takes great pride in its approach to the pollution problem. Water enters the oil business from the beginning, with the wells from which there may be seepage into nearby watercourses, and the salt water that sometimes appears during drilling, all the way through a refining process that uses seven gallons of water for cooling every gallon of gasoline. Water even serves as a passageway, in the form of rivers and seas, over which oil products are carried to consumers. At every step of the way there is danger of accidental contamination.

When the Shell Oil Company proposed building a refinery at Anacortes near Seattle on Puget Sound, there was much alarm among local conservationists concerning the oyster beds in waters near the planned location. With great care Shell demonstrated just how pure the water would be at the end of the refining process—so pure, in fact, that it has to be piped half a mile out to sea to bypass the oysters which require saltier water. Today, the bivalves and the refinery are living happily as next-door neighbors.

At the Humble Oil Company plant in Baytown, Texas, there is a large reservoir where effluent water is treated for a full six weeks. It is stocked with fish whose continued health is a guarantee of its purity; then the water is discharged into the Houston Ship Channel and down into Galveston Bay, where fish thrive in great numbers.

The oil industry uses water in enormous amounts, but doesn't use it up. After use, the water is treated to make it as clean as is technically possible, whereupon it is returned to natural waterways, as it is from most industries. The oil industry in the United States uses about four billion gallons of fresh and salt water daily, and the cost of treating it is correspondingly large. When the industries around the lower end of Lake Michigan were being charged with ruining its water, the Cities Service Oil Company was singled out for its fine record.

In the better drilling operations, the salt water that often appears in oil wells is injected back into underground formations, and smaller amounts of salt water are pumped into rubber-lined pits where they evaporate. Oil pipelines in remote areas are regularly patrolled by small planes to spot breaks and leaks.

Numerous problems for the oil industry are caused by operations at sea. Residents of the East Coast, from Florida north to Massachusetts, can recall the grim days of World War II when the sand beaches were black with oil from torpedoed tankers. The major oil shippers of the world have signed an agreement prohibiting their tankers from discharging near shore, but there are probably many independent tankers that still foul the sea with their oily waste. Shell Oil, British Petroleum, and Esso are among the major fleet operators which have devised ingenious methods for getting rid of ballast, and which also take special precautions to prevent spillage during loading and discharging.

The oil companies are particularly sensitive to public relations about the problems of pollution, perhaps because they distribute directly to the consumer, who can retaliate by boycotting their product. (Standard of California regularly has to prove that oil in the sea off El Segundo comes from a natural seepage on the bottom, and has nothing to do with its refinery.)

Other Industries

It would seem, from the histories of the Mahoning River and Lake Erie, that the makers and users of steel are less aware of their responsibilities for good water to the public, perhaps because the public seldom knows whose steel it is using. Nevertheless, the Republic Steel plant at Birmingham and Great Lakes Steel at Detroit are now substituting hydrochloric acid for the sulphuric acid that is traditionally used to clean new steel of the rust induced by water cooling. The remains of this process were called "pickle likker," and once caused streams near steel mills to run red. The hydrochloric acid now in use is washed clear of the rust and used over again.

Bethlehem Steel points with pride to its new plant at Burns Harbor, Michigan, where a deep well has been drilled to accept waste fluid. The well leads down to a deep natural formation, from which it will take between eighty and ninety years to seep as far as Lake Michigan.

The wood-pulp industry is a great user of water and has been a serious polluter. In fact, it would appear that Senator Muskie, chairman of the committee dedicated to passing tough water-pollution bills, must derive some of his zeal from what he learned as governor of the paper-producing state of Maine. To show that they had the best interests of the country at heart, the producers of paper and pulp have organized the National Council for Stream Improvement. This is positive thinking indeed, in an industry accused of messing up streams. The Council conducts research on solutions to the industries' pollution problems. It maintains regional research centers at five universities. The Council states that the average pollution load per ton of paper has been reduced by 65 per cent in the last twenty years, and that three-quarters of its member mills have installed water treatment facilities—which still leaves a certain distance to be traveled.

Organic wastes from paper milling are hard to break down and much research goes into ways of providing extra oxygen to do the job. New paper plants that are being built have very advanced systems for treating waste water. The new Kimberly-Clark factory near Sacramento turns out water so clean that healthy salmon play in the millions of gallons of it that are discharged daily. This is a hopeful sign for the future, and an interesting contrast to a stream in New England with so much waste pulp on the bottom that it cannot even be removed by a dredge—and to the International Paper

Company plant on Lake Champlain, which discharges, according to the official complaint of Vermont residents, "a whole river of filthy liquid and scum and foam daily into the lake which is nauseating in both sight and smell."

Chemicals are the fastest-growing large industry in the United States today. Much of the activity is centered on the Kanawha River around Charleston, West Virginia, one of the great chemical complexes of the world. A booklet issued by a Washington group, Resources for the Future, Inc., points out, "It is in areas of heavy industry and dense population, where the need for outdoor recreation facilities is the greatest, that industrial effluents and municipal wastes are likely to have spoiled the beauty and usability of nearby waters for recreational purposes." In other words, the employees of the chemical companies wanted to use the Kanawha for fun, and complained when they found it too dirty.

The du Pont Corporation, which has one of the largest plants on the river, discovered through a special study that during its manufacture of various products, about 300 million gallons of polluted cooling water were being discharged every day into the Kanawha River. In cooperation with nine other industrial firms on that stream, du Pont engaged in an abatement program that has reduced pollution by even more than was required by the authorities. This program costs the plant an extra $1 million or more a year to operate—an indication as to why industries oppose the regulation of what they do to rivers.

The du Pont, Dow, and Monsanto chemical companies are all working on the problems caused by the exotic wastes produced by an industry that is always bringing out new products. These are wastes that nature has no way of absorbing or breaking down. They are now being buried thousands of feet below ground, in areas where they cannot contaminate the ground water. Other techniques of disposal are being tried—

radical processes that may ultimately have application in pollution problems unconnected with the chemical business.

Detergents

The most completely successful step against water pollution by industry has been taken by the manufacturers of detergents. These products did not break down biologically in streams and rivers, and left very visible quantities of suds. Consumers had become acutely aware of detergent pollution, and in some places in Europe detergents had already been forbidden by law. The industry, after ten years of very expensive but completely voluntary research, has found a way to make detergents that do break down biologically. All detergents sold since June 1965 have been of this kind.

It is obvious how dramatic all the bustling business activity in the United States has made the pollution problem. Though much is being done, it is still very much with us. But at least nowadays no one pretends that the problem isn't there or that it will somehow go away; almost everyone agrees that some control at least is necessary for the common good. No longer does any American community point to a polluted river as a sign of local prosperity. Many communities are even becoming embarrassed by all the pollution caused by their constantly growing populations.

9

We Can't All Live Upstream

GUILTY CITIES

CITY systems to prevent water pollution from sewage are a surprisingly recent development. Those American soldiers who during World War II disliked France because of its plumbing would no doubt have been startled to be told that at that time 60 million of their own countrymen had no sewerage system at all. Even in the prosperous America of today, 65 million are served by no municipal sewer system, and towns with a total population of 15 million throw sewage without any treatment at all into our rivers and streams. The rich United States can hardly boast about being sanitary.

Plumbing-conscious Americans may be surprised to learn that only a little more than a hundred years ago Boston's best hotel, which was also the best in the United States, had 170 guest rooms and only eight bathrooms, all of those in the basement. New York City at the same time had a population of 630,000 people and only 10,000 toilets. Modern plumbing, which puts so tremendous a load upon the water supply, became a preoccupation only when it was discovered during an epidemic of cholera in London that the source of the disease was a contaminated community pump. Then it became obvious that large cities had to deal with the problem of sewage disposal to avoid what would amount to suicide. Even so, in 1900 the death rate in the United States from water-borne typhoid was thirty-five for every 100,000. It was not until 1908 that cities began to add chlorine to purify their water. For some reason the addition of this chemical to assist the public health did not create the hysterical controversy that greeted the later addition of fluoride.

Though filtration and chlorination assured all United States cities of safe drinking water they were still reckless about what happened to water that had been used. Most cities gave it only primary treatment, meaning that visible particles were removed and the remainder piped to some river or lake where the oxygen in the water was supposed to do the rest of the work. If the next town downstream happened to be ten or fifteen miles away, and so long as the towns remained fairly small, this method was effective, and the water could be safely used again. When, however, cities a hundred or so miles downstream had to begin spending large amounts of money to get pure water—and then only by adding so many chemicals that it had a bad taste—there was pressure for secondary treatment of waste water, a system whereby wastes would be held in solution until they were consumed by bacteria.

The construction of secondary-treatment plants has been accelerated in recent years, but it has barely kept ahead of the growth in population. At the present rate of development, there will by 1970 be 85 million people in the United States living outside any sewerage system.

One problem that is bound to loom larger in the future concerns all the suburban homes and developments that have been built with cesspools rather than municipal systems.

Cesspools are by no means foolproof, and often leak into ground water that is pumped for drinking purposes.

Another problem of cities that try to save money is the practice of combining sewer systems with those used for storm drainage. When after a heavy rain the sewage disposal plant is unable to handle the volume of water, the overflow is simply drained into the watercourse. This happens regularly at the plants around southern Lake Michigan, and is part of the reason why beaches as far away as Milwaukee are so often closed. A curious fact is that rain itself acts as a pollutant: as it falls on city roofs, paved sidewalks, and streets, all the soot, oil, and animal refuse that would have soaked into the ground, where the water would have been purified, now flows, full of filth, into the storm drains.

The same situation occurs at the beaches around New York City, which often have to be closed after rainstorms. Until 1966 New York City had secondary treatment for 900 million gallons of sewage daily, leaving on an average an additional 300 million gallons to be dumped raw into the Hudson, Harlem, and East rivers. A new plant at Newtown Creek will handle most of this, but the storm drainage problem continues.

New York State voters in 1965 approved a $1 billion bond issue for funds to be spent in the next six years to overcome that state's many pollution problems. The legislature approved putting this bond issue on the ballot by a unanimous vote. Awareness of the problem had reached even the rural areas that dominate the state government. In urging approval of the bill, Governor Rockefeller pointed out that pollution jeopardized health, lowered property values, restricted the expansion of industry, and destroyed recreation. He also pointed out the existence of drought-stricken areas where pollution prevented the inhabitants from using their own water, and of 1167 towns where the sewage was being discharged raw or was at best poorly treated.

At one time the city of Philadelphia had a reputation for bad-tasting water. It draws its supply from the heavily industrialized Delaware and Schuylkill rivers, which almost make it an island. Twenty years ago the rivers were grossly polluted from chemicals and detergents, dead vegetation, industrial and animal wastes. Most of the sewage went into the rivers raw; the waters were killing fish and driving away shipping. Then, beginning in 1946, the city made an enormous investment to improve its water supply. With the help of the states of Pennsylvania and New Jersey, Philadelphians prodded numerous other towns upstream to build sewage plants. Industries were urged to begin treating their wastes; the Army Engineers did extensive dredging to clean up the Schuylkill River bottom; a Delaware River Basin Commission was formed. All sewage from Philadelphia now gets secondary treatment, and citizens no longer need to buy bottled drinking water.

In 1948 less than 1 per cent of the sewage discharged into the Ohio River, whose valley then had a population of ten million people, was purified. Not only did drinking water taste bad; even the propellers on boats were corroded by the acid in the river. That year all eight of the states along the banks of the Ohio joined forces in an agency known as ORSANCO to act on the deplorable conditions. The approval of Congress to act as a unit and the expenditure of a billion dollars have produced treatment plants covering all but 1 per cent of the population along the river. All but 8 per cent of the 1700 industrial establishments along the river who discharge effluents are complying with at least minimum control requirements.

After this sizable achievement, member states of ORSANCO were not altogether pleased to be summoned to a conference by the Public Health Service to discuss conditions on the tributary Monongahela River. At the conclusion it was agreed that the states were doing a very good job, except on sulphuric acid drainage from coal mines—a problem that occurs when rain water combines with the sulphur that is always found in conjunction with coal, to form the acid, which then seeps downhill, leaving a black swath of dead plants and animals. The states and the federal government agreed to continue looking for a solution and in the fall of 1965, over loud protests, Pennsylvania passed a law that any mine from which acid was found to be draining was to be closed down. Meanwhile, the Ohio has become clean enough to attract pleasure boats—which bring in a brand-new source of pollution as they discharge oil waste, sewage, and garbage.

While the Public Health Service was throwing its weight around investigating pollution, someone asked what the federal government itself was doing. A search revealed that it was in fact a major polluter. Sixty-eight federal installations, mostly military bases, were found to be dumping millions of gallons of untreated sewage daily. Congress hurriedly appropriated money to build treatment plants and ordered the Public Health Service to keep a closer watch in the future.

During the Public Health Service investigation of Lake Erie, the city of Detroit was found, along with its industries, to be making massive contributions to the ill health of the lake. Its sewage was receiving no more than primary treatment. City officials were indignant at being ordered to install secondary treatment, and complained that the system would cost them $100 million—though since the city has almost two million people living in it, such an expenditure would hardly cause bankruptcy. It is thought that Detroit will finally comply. In recent years St. Louis and Kansas City have changed to secondary treatment without any signs of hardship. The State and various cities of California have spent over $1 billion in the last fifteen years, and it is boasted that out of a population of 14 million people, only 17,000 live in towns without treatment plants.

Impressive as all this spending of money is, the continued

growth of population means that new methods of handling pollution must be constantly studied. One that has been suggested is to aerate the rivers so as to speed up biological decomposition. Another is to build more reservoirs that will hold water back until times of low flow, when it can be released to flush out turgid streams. Another is to pipe sewage long distances and discharge it far away from population centers.

New Developments in Treating Waste

Space research has stimulated much thinking about the re-use of water. In a spaceship that will be away from earth for weeks or months, supplying water and getting rid of wastes is necessarily a closed-cycle operation. Four volunteers at the Aerojet General Corporation in Azusa, California, who for eight weeks drank nothing but water reconverted from waste, showed no adverse physiological symptoms.

At San Francisco the Navy's Hydro Program is working on effective methods of burning waste. A scientist at General Electric foresees a time when every house will have equipment for cleaning up the water to make it usable again and again. To put people into a frame of mind for this, he suggests that such water be used first for watering lawns and washing cars. Even so, such schemes appear to be still some distance in the future.

Research on what appears today to be the most promising method called Advanced Waste Water Treatment, has its headquarters at the Public Health Service office in Cincinnati. The center has been named for Robert A. Taft but has no other political significance—though ultimate success here may eliminate argument among many political and economic groups.

The aim of the project is simply to answer the question,

what happens to the water we use every day? In an experiment at Lebanon, Ohio, water is used again and again after being treated by chemical, electrical, and physical methods that go far beyond the standard secondary treatment in an effort to make it absolutely pure. The cost of treating water this way is admittedly high, and the research is intended to find out the least expensive way of doing it.

Of the program's two stated objectives,

one is to help abate our nation's growing water pollution problem, and the other, more startling in concept, is to renovate waste water for direct and deliberate re-use. Waste waters are this country's most immediately available water resource. They do not have to be pumped over mountains or from deep underground resources. If we can learn how to remove the contaminants from these waters efficiently and economically, than these waters can be used again and again. In one such step such a new technology *would alleviate both our water pollution and water supply problems.*

The measure of success in advanced waste water treatment is economics. Complete water renovation is already possible, but at unreasonably high costs. Tomorrow's economics, however, must apply rather than today's. It is unlikely that a new technology will provide water at today's costs, but these costs cannot continue much longer in any case. We will soon reach the time when rivers and streams can no longer assimilate our wastes, and also the time when no more supplies of fresh water are available. A new water technology will then be a necessity.

Similar experiments are being made at Sycamore Canyon, near San Diego, where reconstituted water fills a lake that is being used for swimming, fishing, and boating—with the public fully aware of where the water came from. The water costs only slightly more than that from the Colorado, and is actually purer. Another plant, at Whittier Narrows near Los Angeles, produces ten million gallons of reconstituted water daily, and pumps it into the soil to replenish lost ground water. Purified waste water is likewise being used to build up the ground water supply on Long Island.

Advanced Waste Water Treatment will, unfortunately, some day produce a brand-new set of pollution problems—as public-spirited water treatment has already done. The residue of the process makes excellent fertilizer. Like the fertilizer-filled runoff of farms that has added to the problems around Lake Erie and that has caused Lake Tahoe to bloom with algae, the residue causes plant life to flourish. The wilderness area of the Superior National Forest along the border between Minnesota and Canada is served by the little town of Ely, which duly gives its sewage secondary treatment. What is left over is dumped into nearby Lake Sagawa, which as a result is full of weeds. Officials in New York City, from which the daily residue is taken by barge fourteen miles out to sea, were worried about the effect this might have on fish—and the complaints of fishermen. At first there were objections, but then the area was found to be the best one for bluefish in the entire world.

There are studies at the Taft Center at Cincinnati of various possibilities for disposing of the residue—including chemical means, burning (which would contribute to air pollution), and, inevitably, the ocean. Pipelines extending from as far inland as the Twin Cities to some place out at sea, are being visualized. What effect this would finally have on life in the sea is anybody's guess, and may turn out to be a problem for the next generation to solve.

What is encouraging today is the almost universal recognition that everybody, in fact, lives downstream—plus the steps that are being taken so we can all live there safely.

10

Controlling the Wild Element

EVEN assuming that effective control of pollution is in sight—and this in itself seems unduly optimistic—the question remains whether there will be *enough* water for all the country's growing needs.

The average daily rainfall in the United States is 4200 billion gallons—an astronomical amount of water, most of which evaporates without being used. Nevertheless, 1200 billion gallons of that daily total do become available. Since the total amount of water being used at present is 370 billion gallons, there might seem to be a considerable amount left over. What is misleading about averages like this is that the water does not always fall where it is needed. Rainfall has been measured at 140 inches a year in the Cascade Mountains of Washington, while southern California with its ten million people gets only about eleven inches a year. Much water is lost by runoff into the sea. There are estimates that it will not be economical to recover more than 700 billion gallons a day, or double what is being used at present. When it is projected that by the year 2000 the demand will have risen to 900 billion gallons a day, it becomes clear what a dilemma we face.

The hope for an answer is in water's constant re-use. Water from the Ohio River is used an average of almost four times before it flows into the Mississippi. Agriculture in the region is currently using about 140 billion gallons a day of water that doesn't return to earth in the form of rain for some time.

The Bethlehem Steel Company at Sparrows Point, Maryland, offers an example of what happens to the rest. The company's use of 150 million gallons a day was putting it into competition with the city of Baltimore for ground-water supplies. The solution was very simple: steel-making does not require water of absolute purity, so Bethlehem now buys treated water from the Baltimore sewer system. Impressed with the success of Bethlehem, a number of plants now use "polished" municipal waste water, particularly in the dry Southwest. So do a number of golf courses and irrigation systems.

Projections of the demand for water in the future are based on the ways in which water is used at the present time, particularly by industry. Technology may make it possible to get along on a good deal less. The Kaiser Steel Company at Fontana, in dry southern California, uses only one-tenth the amount of water required in older plants.

On the other hand, the best laid plans of men have a way of going wrong. After a fairly severe drought during the 1950s, New York City was so confidently believed to have solved its water problems by the construction of two new, large reservoirs on the Delaware River, that the year 2000 held no terrors. But before the new reservoirs could be filled, another drought struck and lasted five years. As the available water supply sank lower and lower, there were panic reactions. Politicians suddenly became water experts and offered some bizarre solutions to the problems. Water meters were demanded, though they would take five years to install and would put no effective pressure on apartment renters who make up most of the population. An atomic-powered desalting plant was planned for Riverhead, New York, though its production of a million gallons a day would be feebly small. Leaky faucets were sought out, and the citizens were urged to conserve—moves that seemed pretty pointless, with repeated breaks in the hundred-year-old system of water mains conspicuously flooding the streets. The Hudson River, which had been flowing past at the rate of 11 billion gallons a day, was at last tapped, a job made more difficult by the immense amount of filth poured into it from towns along its entire length. The federal government finally took official cognizance of the problem, and the Army Engineers began studying ways to join the Northeast together in one gigantic water system whereby water could be diverted to any area badly in need. The Engineers have their eyes on the St. Lawrence River, the government of Canada permitting, and on other sources as far west as ruined Lake Erie. For New York, however, the immediate prospect is that the Hudson River, the logical source, will be cleaned up and used to supply the city's water.

Desalination

Although water refined from the sea probably can never solve the problems of enormous cities, it is already being used in special situations where the cost is a secondary problem. The Westinghouse Company first became interested in taking salt out of brackish water, so that it could be used in electric power plants, as long ago as 1930. After World War II, Westinghouse engineers were called in by the hot and arid sheikdom of Kuwait, which had recently been discovered to have the world's greatest reserves of oil but had hardly any water to make life bearable for British and American oil men. The desalting plant Westinghouse built there now produces five million gallons a day—admittedly at a high cost. One of the problems to be overcome was that the Persian

Gulf is one of the world's saltiest bodies of water. Later Westinghouse built a demonstration plant at San Diego—now famous for having been dismantled and shipped to Guantanamo Bay in Cuba when Fidel Castro cut off the water supply there. Today Westinghouse has more than fifty desalting units in coastal cities of such places as Indonesia, Aruba, the Virgin Islands, and the Canary Islands off Africa. There is even a tiny plant on the island of Guernsey, in the English Channel, where about every eight years a drought threatens the valuable tomato crop.

Other firms now in the desalting business include one based in Washington, D.C., which has built a plant able to distill more than two million gallons a day for the town of Key West, Florida. Previously the town had been dependent on a long pipeline from Miami. The United States government has announced joint plans with Mexico for a nuclear-powered desalting plant in the Gulf of California, which will produce around 100 million gallons a day.

Making water from the sea fit to drink is not a new idea. It goes back to Julius Caesar, who used solar evaporators during his siege of Alexandria in 49 B.C. But there had been little progress since, until the prospect of shortages made the need unmistakably clear. The idea that has received the most publicity has been the use of nuclear fuel for the job. The first nuclear-powered desalting apparatus was the one aboard the submarine *Nautilus*. The entire fleet of nuclear submarines and the nuclear cargo ship *Savannah* are now likewise equipped, and the Navy has also constructed a small nuclear unit on McMurdo Sound in the Antarctic. All of these are, of course, very special applications, and it is generally believed that desalting the sea will not be economically feasible in plants producing less than 50 million gallons a day. Prospects for plants of this size are being studied in southern California and in Israel. The project has been backed by President Johnson, who denies that desalination is "a far out and distant goal," and during the drought of the 1960s Congress voted additional funds to speed it up. However, even if the cost of nuclear-produced water could be brought down to twenty-five or thirty cents per thousand gallons, it would still be too expensive to use for irrigation.

The Department of the Interior has set up an office to test methods of obtaining fresh water. In many areas of the United States and throughout the world, water that is not as salty as the sea, but is still brackish, may be made potable by a process of electrodialysis, now being tried experimentally at Webster, South Dakota; by freezing, as in an experiment at Wrightsville Beach, North Carolina; or by distillation, as at Roswell, New Mexico and Freeport, Texas. Freeport has already piped a billion gallons of fresh water into the city system, but at a cost of one dollar per thousand gallons, much more than Americans normally pay. In the future a promising method known as reverse osmosis will be given a trial at some water-starved location. In regular use today are productive, but expensive, desalting plants at Coalinga, California, and Buckeye, Arizona.

One novel proposal has been to use the sea's own thermal energy in desalting it. The process would take advantage of the difference in temperature between deep and surface waters. That this is possible was proved by French engineers operating in the tropical waters off Africa's Ivory Coast. The best method may, of course, turn out to be some new scientific discovery nobody has yet thought of.

Rainmakers

Such scientific discoveries are certainly needed when it comes to increasing our water supply by modifying the weather, or "rainmaking." The hope, according to the National Science Foundation, is "to acquire knowledge permitting us to minimize the number and severity of hurricanes, tornadoes and other violent storms and, also, to be able to improve the temperature and rainfall in agricultural and industrial regions." This heady undertaking is certainly as important as developing nuclear energy or putting a man on the moon, but it is many steps behind both. The scientific principles of nuclear reactors and space travel are well in hand, but the physics of the interaction between air and sea are very imperfectly understood. Since it is not even known what makes rain, how can anyone be sure that silver iodide crystals have ever really made it fall?

Though the Indians of the Southwest have danced their appeals to the rain god for centuries, and though *The Rainmaker* was the title of a very interesting play, it is only in recent years that weather modification has been a serious subject for science.

Project Stormfury, run jointly by the Navy and what used to be known as the Weather Bureau, is now concerned with finding a way to control or at least to steer hurricanes. (The explanation for the fact that hurricanes are named after girls is that their names are easier to remember than boys' names, numbers, or the letters of the Greek alphabet. There is less confusion if there are two in action. A name is retired for ten years if it is attached to a major storm.) A medium-sized hurricane releases as much energy in a day as a thousand atom bombs the size of the one dropped on Hiroshima. Weather modifiers therefore now make it a rule not to tamper with storms that have any possibility of reaching land, though they once seeded a hurricane which turned landward and hit Georgia with a snowstorm in August. No one is certain, however, that the experiment had anything to do with that event. The seeding is done by dropping a silver iodide bomb into the center or eye of the storm, in an effort to cool off the great masses of hot air. After such a test, hurricane Beulah registered a drop of thirty knots in wind velocity, and the air pressure rose fifteen points, but the experimenters are not yet ready to assert that their work was the cause. The silver iodide technique is also being used by the Forest Service in its Project Skyfire, whose purpose is to bring rain that will put out fires caused by lightning. In this the Service says it has had considerable success.

A new idea for taming hurricanes has come out of the discovery that twice as much heat energy in hurricanes comes from the surface of the sea as from the atmosphere. It is thought that if a thin film of oil could be spread on the water the escape of much of the heat by evaporation could be prevented and the storm would be denied its source of strength. The problem is to find an oil that would produce such an effect in winds of sixty miles an hour or more.

On the other hand, some scientists question whether it is a good idea even to try to control hurricanes, since, in spite of the damage they cause, they bring much needed rainfall to the south and east of the United States.

There are some bizarre military possibilities that open up with the ability to control weather. Could an enemy's harbor be frozen up so that his ships could not get out? Could rockets or balloons be sent over enemy territory to create a heavy fog that would ground all his aircraft? If we melted the Arctic icecap, would the change in weather and currents help us and make the enemy's weather worse? In what ways might such activities backfire?

And within the government itself there are divergent views on the entire subject of weather modification. The Bureau of Reclamation has experiments with cloud-seeding in South Dakota, in Wyoming, and on the west side of the Colorado Rockies. The last of those is the most promising, since silver iodide apparently works best in mountain country where there are already clouds with rain in them. The Bureau expects no conclusive results for at least ten years, although meanwhile the tests may be useful in settling legal claims that have arisen out of previous rain-making experiments, and there are hopes of producing some extra snow to augment the flow of the Colorado River.

Officials of the National Science Foundation take the view that this is all very premature, that there is a great possibility of adverse consequences and too little knowledge for a proper evaluation of the results. They believe that the triggering mechanisms for weather can be analyzed by means of computers without the hazard, for example, of a live experiment ending a drought in the Great Plains but also bringing a killing frost to Florida.

The Army Engineers

Of more immediate effect on our water supply is the work of the Army Engineers and the Bureau of Reclamation in building dams. The story of the Engineers begins logically in Minnesota at the headwaters of the Mississippi, the river they first attempted to control.

In its first hundred miles, the Mississippi flows through four very large lakes, and this assures a fairly constant supply of water throughout the year. The region is also one of heavy snowfall, and in the spring the river and its tributary the Minnesota can be expected to flood, sometimes heavily. There is little the Engineer Corps can do about this. The river is old; it has worn down most of its banks and there are no convenient canyons, as there are in the West, where flood-control dams might be built. There are so many towns and farms along the riverside that any such construction would mean great hardship and economic loss. The residents take their chances philosophically. These days, at least, they get considerable warning before a flood arrives.

The Engineers nevertheless, have built a series of dams on the upper river, mainly to provide a nine-foot channel for navigation throughout the year. Though the dams may have a slight effect in controlling floods, what they really do is turn the river into a canal through a series of lakes. An unplanned benefit is that the upper river from the Twin Cities to St. Louis is excellent for boating, although most people hesitate to swim in it. Commercial river traffic has grown enormously over the years, and the number of barges continues to increase.

The body responsible for turning the upper Mississippi into a canal is an unusual one, which from its name would seem to have little to do with controlling floods and making deep-river channels. The involvement of the Army Engineers in such projects goes back to the time of the Revolutionary War, when the only men with a European background in engineering were Army officers. The first engineering school in the United States was at West Point. Thus it was that before the Civil War, when Congress decided to improve the Mississippi for navigation, it quite logically turned to the Army. Of the more than twenty federal agencies concerned with water resources today, the Corps of Engineers is the oldest.

The first levees on the Mississippi had been built in 1727, and construction went on piecemeal throughout the years. Since levees were thought to be the concern of individual landowners, the Corps' first work on the river was to remove snags and flood-borne logs that endangered traffic below the mouth of the stream.

At the junction where the Yazoo River, the second biggest tributary on the eastern side of the Mississippi, enters near Vicksburg, high water once regularly covered about half of the rich delta land during four or five months out of every year. To protect their holdings, individual farmers built their own private levees to keep the water out, thus enraging farmers downstream where the floods rose even higher. At times of high water the private levees had to be patrolled by armed guards to prevent their being dynamited. Shotguns thus became an implement of flood control. The farmers agreed to community-wide drainage control only during World War I, with its enormous demand for the cotton they grew.

Severe floods have been commonplace on the lower Mississippi and through the nation's history, but Congress did nothing to interfere with such acts of God until the disaster of 1927, when 637,000 people were displaced by the rampaging river. In that year Congress authorized the Army Corps of Engineers to undertake its first project in flood control. It is the boast of the Engineers that they have kept the river below St. Louis in hand ever since. (It is probably unfair to repeat that the streets of New Orleans were underwater in the fall of 1965. That, after all, was caused by a hurricane and was therefore the province of the Navy or the Weather Bureau.)

The Engineers have built levees, revetments, cutoffs, reservoirs, floodways, and spillways at a cost of $1.4 billion, and the project is about two-thirds complete. They estimate they have prevented $7.25 billion worth of flood damage since 1928. Dependable navigation and the great supply of fresh water on the safely shackled lower valley, once a completely agricultural region, have attracted a vast industrial complex, now that it is, according to the Engineers, "proof against anything but a flood of continental dimensions never yet known."

Having taken the Mississippi in their stride and having practically invented the science of hydrology in the process, the Engineers turned to the Ohio, which in spring carries more water than the upper Mississippi. The Ohio Valley is heavily industrialized, and factories crowd so close to the water's edge that reservoirs on the main river have had to be considered out of the question. They were built instead on its many tributaries, each of which has been canalized like the main river. Since 1930, when the system went into operation, the total amount of barge traffic has increased four times over.

When Lewis and Clark first explored the unknown land acquired by the Louisiana Purchase, they traveled up the Missouri River. The longest river in the United States, it has always been one of the most troublesome, as it constantly changes course over a wide flat plain. During the expedition, as is usual, periods of wild flooding alternated with periods of intense drought, making navigation on the river quite unpredictable.

Writing for the *American Magazine* in 1907, the humorist George Fitch observed that there were all sorts of rivers, with varying degrees of wetness and varying claims to fame.

> But there is only one river with a personality, habits, dissipations, a sense of humor, and a woman's caprice; a river that goes traveling sidewise, that interferes in politics, rearranges geography, and dabbles in real estate; a river that plays hide and seek with you today and tomorrow follows you around like a pet dog with a dynamite cracker tied to its tail.
>
> The Missouri River was located in the United States at last reports. It cuts corners, runs around at night, lunches on levees, and swallows islands and small villages for dessert. Its perpetual dissatisfaction with its bed is the greatest peculiarity of the Missouri. Time after time it has gotten out of its bed in the middle of the night, with no apparent provocation, and has hunted up a new bed, all littered with forests, cornfields, brick houses, railroad ties, and telegraph poles. Later it has suddenly taken a fancy to its old

bed, which by this time has been filled with suburban architecture, and back it has gone with a whoop and a rush as if it had really found something worthwhile.

It makes farming as fascinating as gambling. You never know whether you are going to harvest corn or catfish.

Beginning in 1943, the Engineers made a study of what could be done with the Missouri. At about the same time the Bureau of Reclamation of the Department of the Interior made a separate study. Why two federal departments should have been assigned to the same river is a matter of interest and confusion to students of government.

Be that as it may, the combined results, known as the Pick-Sloan Plan, call for the construction of more than a hundred dams and reservoirs on the river and its tributaries, plus levees and a navigable channel from Sioux City, Iowa, to the river's mouth. The project will irrigate millions of acres of farmland and provide billions of kilowatt hours of electricity, in addition to controlling floods. The upper reaches of the Missouri River often have very low rainfall. The lower river has plenty of rain, but has often been devastated by floods. The plan gives each area that particular dominance it needs over the wide Missouri. It has been theorized that if the Missouri had been taken in hand early enough, the widespread suffering and financial loss during the period of the Dust Bowl in the 1930s could have been avoided, and hundreds of thousands of people would not have emigrated west.

The Fort Peck dam, the first built under the plan, was at one time the largest earthen dam in the world. During the disastrous flood of 1952 it held the river all by itself, and it is credited with saving the cities of Omaha and Council Bluffs. Since then five enormous new dams have been completed, two of which have created lakes over a hundred miles long. Anyone who has traveled in this dry region can imagine how welcome the man-made lakes must be to those who live there.

Much of the multibillion dollar cost of all this will be returned through the sale of hydroelectric power, quite aside from the considerable savings as a result of keeping floods under control.

The Corps of Engineers has also set up flood control projects on a smaller scale. One of these is on the Willamette River in Oregon, where in the winter of 1964 dams saved the city of Portland from severe flooding, after a third of a normal year's rain fell in nine days. Dams in northern California are credited with preventing hundreds of millions of dollars' worth of damage by the same freak storm.

A continuing activity of the Corps is its study of how mankind can live on flood plains, those areas attractive to farming, industry, and recreation, which rivers have repeatedly claimed as their own. The best answer seems to be a compromise with the facts of life along the river: when new buildings are put up, very little of value is put on the ground floor where it might be ruined by floods.

The Corps has been responsible for building the various inland waterways, for the operation of the St. Lawrence Seaway, for navigation and water depths on the Great Lakes, and for hundreds of different harbor projects. Recently it took part in studies leading to the construction of a new canal, to be excavated by nuclear energy, that would supplement the Panama Canal in Central America. The Corps has also taken part in the Appalachia development program. When it became official policy to make America beautiful again, the Corps pointed proudly to the hundreds of glorious lakes it has created, the splendid dams themselves and the river banks that are no longer littered by floods, and to its contribution toward rebuilding the riverfronts of St. Louis and Pittsburgh.

Still another responsibility of the Army Corps of Engineers are the sandy beaches along the coasts. The beaches are endangered in a number of ways. The rise in sea level, though barely perceptible, poses a threat to the sandy shore. Storms and hurricanes wash beaches away, and the supply of sand that normally replaces them—the leached and eroded soil washed into the sea by rivers—is now being reduced by better methods of farming, by dams that hold back eroded earth, and by the decrease in the amount of water that is allowed by man to reach the sea. In southern California, where a very limited amount of water is permitted to get to the ocean, the beaches are quite visibly receding.

The diminution of this natural resource is very incompletely understood. To save what remains of it on the south shore of Long Island, the Engineers have started an experiment that consists of laying out great boulders, to form what they call a groin, at right angles to the beach in the hope of keeping the sand in place. At Newport, Rhode Island, the Engineers have also had to deal with angry residents, who rose up in indignation over proposed new hurricane barriers, which they feared would interfere with their yachting.

Angry voices were also raised against the Engineers after the drought of 1965 began to affect the Florida Everglades. As long ago as 1926, a hurricane overflowed the vast waters of Lake Okeechobee and killed hundreds of people. When the same thing occurred two years later, several thousands were killed. Congress at the behest of President Hoover decided to act, and the Corps was ordered to build a massive series of dikes around the lake to keep the water in however great the storm.

Meanwhile, just to the south, the Everglades State Park was set aside, and much of the swamp was drained. When the drought arrived in 1965, the waters of the lake were needed to save the alligators and other wildlife in the park—but those waters were not to be had. The existing canals were not capable of diverting them in sufficient amounts, and anyway much of the lake had already been drained off as a safeguard against the next probable hurricane—which arrived, more or less on schedule, a few months later.

Without deciding the merits of the argument that resulted, it is clear that there hadn't been sufficient area-wide planning. In the words of one of the Corps' most articulate spokesmen, "If there is one fact that is basic to all others in the water resource field, it is that *whenever you do anything to water or related land resources,* you affect *all* other use of those resources everywhere in that basin. This is the reason why water-resource planning and development form such a complex, intricate field."

The Army Corps of Engineers is a very big business. It affects every state in the Union, and every individual American as well. It spends billions of dollars every year and has been accused—not without justice—of maintaining one of the best lobbies on Capitol Hill. Its huge projects have become the *bêtes noirs* of other bureaucracies in the government that might have used the same appropriation themselves. The Engineers have irritated state and local authorities, conservationists, and—as soon as they become aware of all the money being spent—numerous taxpayers. They have been accused of being power-hungry, of moving into areas of activity where they have no business, and of building dams just for the sake of building dams.

In response a General in the Corps has said;

> Those of us who have a part in the responsibility for keeping track of the nation's water availabilities and needs are sometimes accused of being overly ambitious when we try to explain the implications of our fast-growing economy in terms of its future water development requirements. But we would not be true to our responsibilities if we did not give timely warning that this nation is going to need hundreds of new reservoirs and thousands of miles of levee and channel improvement, scores of harbors, millions more acre-feet of water-storage capacity, and billions of

dollars of investment in all kinds of water resource development, if we expect our children to continue to enjoy the advantages of our society in the years to come.

The TVA

One significant stretch of the Mississippi watershed that never came under the control of the Army Corps of Engineers is the tributary system, developed under the Tennessee Valley Authority, which came into being in 1933 and is today one of the most highly developed rivers in the world. Although the Army Engineers run its locks, they have nothing else to do with the TVA. They seem not to have been seriously considered as possible developers of the river, perhaps because at the beginning they had not gone into the power business, but more probably because the whole question became politically so controversial.

The Tennessee River had always been a highway for Indians, and as soon as the first settlers had produce for export—most of it cotton and corn whiskey—they built rafts, flatboats, and keelboats to travel down the river to the Ohio, thence into the Mississippi, and finally to New Orleans. There the produce was disposed of, the craft was sold as timber, and the traders walked home over a long and perilous route known as the Natchez Trace. There was a reason for this: even if they had had power enough, the boatmen would have had trouble on the upstream journey because of a dangerous stretch of water known as Muscle Shoals. Except for an abortive early attempt to build a canal around it, nothing had been done to cope with its turbulent waters before World War I, when it was used as a source of power for a government munitions industry. It was at the conclusion of the war that the Tennessee really got into politics.

The munitions plants at the Shoals were equally well

suited to making nitrate fertilizer. Thanks to the efforts of Senator George Norris of Nebraska, the offers of many large corporations were stoutly resisted. Appalled by the intent to acquire government property for next to nothing, he blocked the sale for fifteen years. Norris had been impressed by the earlier finding of a conservation commission that a river constituted "a unit from its source to the sea," and by the view of the pioneer conservationist Gifford Pinchot that natural resources "made up the one great central problem of the use of the earth for the good of man."

Norris made a number of proposals in Congress for the public operation of Muscle Shoals, only to have each one vetoed—first by President Coolidge and later by President Hoover. By the time Roosevelt was elected, Norris had enlarged his concept still further to envision the TVA. That concept received the Presidential signature in May 1933. The Bureau of Reclamation designed the first dam, and construction was rushed as a means of relieving the desperate nationwide unemployment. Once TVA became law, it still faced numerous difficulties. The private power companies in the area and throughout the country were all dead set against allowing the federal government to go into the power business, and, not content with trying to mobilize public opinion against the project, they took it to court. A presidential candidate in 1940, Wendell Willkie, had made his reputation by opposing it. A Supreme Court decision finally upheld the act.

Both technically and economically, the TVA proved a great success. Power from the dams has provided cheap electricity to the farms and towns of the area, and the former disastrous floods have been controlled. During World War II, when vast amounts of power were needed, among other things, for developing the atomic plant at Oak Ridge, Tennessee, new dams were rushed to completion, and the vision of Senator Norris was finally vindicated.

Since the war TVA has come even more completely into its own. The river is now navigable for 650 miles, and traffic on it increases every year. Over a billion dollars have been spent by private industry for building factories and terminals along its banks. The use of power in the area has increased to such an extent that hydroelectric sources are no longer sufficient, and coal-steam generating plants have had to be built. A new controversy arose over the Dixon-Yates power contract, which would have substituted private power for that produced by TVA. The proposal was defeated, but it showed the persistence of opponents to the very idea of publicly owned power.

A side effect of the project has been the phenomenal growth of recreation on its man-made reservoirs. These are so much prized that when the water level is changed, as must occasionally be done to carry out the original purposes of the development, there is considerable complaint from those who a generation ago viewed the whole idea with suspicion. Another effect of changing the water levels in the TVA lake has been the control of malaria: the lakes are raised a few feet in spring, as the mosquito eggs are about to hatch, and then lowered so that the eggs are stranded and killed by the sun.

TVA still has other, more serious problems. Chattanooga, a city always subject to high water, has so far been protected by the dams from the worst effects of a number of floods, but still needs additional protection against the possibility of future damage. Neither Chattanooga nor Knoxville yet has adequate sewage treatment, and industries in North Carolina, Virginia, and Alabama are still burdening the river with industrial wastes. The owners of a chemical plant in Saltville, Virginia, contend that to control pollution to the required degree would put it out of business, thus raising a question that has been asked before—namely, whether the business is worth saving.

The TVA power system is now the largest in the nation. Its rates for home power consumption are less than half the national average. In 1933 only three farms out of a hundred in the area had electricity; nearly all of them have electricity today. No matter how controversial the TVA may still be at times, its future seems assured.

The Bureau of Reclamation

In the Far West, also, dam-building has brought its share of controversy. Private versus public power has been only one of the disputes; who gets the impounded water is another. Conservationists ask, "Is this dam really necessary?" and do battle to preserve certain noted kinds of fish. They have been so successful in providing safe passage around dams as to cause a spokesman for the Bureau of Reclamation to say, "Every time you eat a can of salmon it really costs five dollars."

Although the Army Corps of Engineers and the Bureau of Reclamation are rival dam-builders today, the Corps had its beginnings in flood control and the Bureau in irrigation. The Bureau was set up in 1902 under the leadership of President Theodore Roosevelt, who took refuge in the Black Hills after the death of his first wife, and who recruited his famous Rough Riders mainly from the state of Texas. At once a romantic and a realist about the West, he saw a great future for it, but only if it had sufficient water. The Bureau of Reclamation was intended to solve this problem by "reclaiming" land that had been water-poor for thousands of years.

The first Reclamation project was in the Salt River Valley of Arizona, where the Hohokam civilization had once thrived and then failed. A dam appropriately named for Roosevelt was built on the river in 1908, and wells powered by it were dug to tap the extensive ground water, which according to geologists may be as much as 4000 years old. Irrigation (and to a much smaller extent, the copper-mining industries, which use and re-use water until it evaporates) is said to be depleting this prehistoric resource at a tremendous rate. The Roosevelt Dam is now old enough to have begun silting up, the irrigators have not completely solved the problem of mineral salts left behind when the water evaporates, and the wells are not being renewed. It is no wonder that the Arizonans, with their rapidly growing cities of Tucson and Phoenix, have all but declared war on California over the water that flows in the Colorado River.

The Controversial Colorado

Aside from small projects on the North Platte in Wyoming and the Milk River in Montana, it was not until 1928 that an act of Congress made possible another major Reclamation project, that of damming Boulder Canyon on the Colorado. The bill was signed by President Hoover, for whom the dam was originally named. Though a Democratic Congress then renamed it Boulder Dam, a still later Congress restored the original name of Hoover Dam, and it remains the crowning accomplishment of the Bureau of Reclamation.

The Colorado carries five cubic miles of water a day—not much as compared to the 770 cubic miles carried daily by the Amazon, but vital in a land that is almost as rainless as the Sahara. The river called "red" by the Spaniards who first found it rises in the snow-capped mountains of central Colorado, zigzags southwest, and finally flows through Mexico into the Gulf of California. Its drainage comprises one-twelfth of the total area of the United States, and it has tributaries from seven western states. Much of its course is through high mesa country, into which it has dug deep chasms, the most spectacular of which is the Grand Canyon. During the settling of the West, the canyon country presented an almost impassable obstacle. After leaving the canyons behind, the river flows through desert where the temperatures have been known to reach 125° Fahrenheit. For many years the Colorado was thought to be a strait that separated California from the mainland.

The first attempts to use the Colorado for irrigation almost ended with the disaster of the Salton Sea. But men who had already traveled that far west through such terrible terrain were not easily persuaded to give up. The town of Yuma on the Mexican border, between the Colorado and Gila rivers, grew up uneasily under the threat of flash floods from both rivers, and in 1916 its levee, a pioneer Reclamation project, was wiped out when the Gila rose, flooding the streets in four feet of water. Because of such troubles with the Gila, the demands grew for secure control of the Colorado, and surveys were begun along its course to discover the best site for a dam.

What emerged was a proposal for a dam high enough to store the entire flow of the Colorado for two entire years, to be placed below almost all the tributaries that were subject to flash floods. Such a dam could produce immense quantities of hydroelectric power. Boulder Canyon, between Nevada and Arizona, was agreed upon as the very best site, but the question that remained was who would get the water.

The law of water-use most commonly in force is that of riparian rights, which entitle the owner to the use of the water that flows through or borders on his land. Most of the far western states, however, have adopted a law of prior appropriation and use, stipulating that whoever got there and used the water first had a perpetual right to it. California had both kinds of law.

It was clear to the six other states containing tributaries to the Colorado that the far more populous California would appropriate and use every possible drop of the dammed-up Colorado River. A compromise was finally reached dividing the river into upper and lower basins, and giving the inhabitants of each basin in perpetuity "the exclusive, beneficial, consumptive use of 7.5 million acre-feet of water annually." Residents of the lower basin could later be permitted to increase their total consumption by one million acre-feet. But the compromise did not apportion the water to the individual states within each of the two basins—an oversight that led to a long and bitter legal controversy between Arizona and California, which began in 1952 and was not settled until 1963, when the Supreme Court handed down a decision as to how much water each state was to receive. Meanwhile, however, the compromise seemed sufficient to permit the construction of the dam to proceed, even though Arizona refused to go along with the agreement until 1944. Funds were authorized with the understanding that the sale of power would entirely repay them, except for the allowance for flood control, within fifty years. It is now estimated that Hoover Dam will be fully paid for in 1983.

To do everything required of it, the dam had to be the highest that had ever been built. When filled, the basin would hold enough water to flood the whole state of New York to a depth of one foot. The dam had also to be big enough to trap the millions of tons of sediment carried by the river every year, without impaired efficiency.

At the time people wondered whether the Southwest could absorb all the power that would be generated. In fact, new power dams have since been constructed to take care of the increased demand. Others were concerned about what the tremendous weight of the lake, 40 billion tons, would do to the crust of the earth. So far, the bedrock on which it lies has experienced no earthquakes. It was thought that the river would be impossible to control during construction and that the dam would fill up with sediment too fast for it to have a useful life. In fact, the river was controlled and the new Glen Canyon Dam upstream, with its additional capacity to hold silt, has now given Hoover Dam at least one hundred years' more life. The greatest worry was about what would happen if the dam should burst after it was put up—certainly a reasonable cause for concern if you lived downstream.

Regardless of these objections, in 1930, with signs of a depression in the air, word came from Washington to rush construction. The dam, one of the great engineering achievements in history, was finished two years ahead of schedule, and was dedicated by President Franklin Roosevelt in May 1935.

The red waters of the Colorado are blue now in the long lake that has backed up behind the man-made barrier. The once impassable spot has become a national recreation area, and swarms with tourists throughout the year. There is no more drought; lands irrigated from the Colorado produce vegetables in the sunny climate from January to December. The most dangerous river in America has been beautifully tamed.

The achievement of Hoover Dam, and particularly its vital role in the growth of Los Angeles, has been so well advertised that people living in distant parts of the country might well wonder why the Bureau of Reclamation is interested in doing anything else to the Colorado River. The answer is that, though their original role was "to assist in making the western United States habitable, primarily by use of water for crop production," they now see that "the end objective is improved national and regional strength and well-being through enlightened use of the natural resources with which our nation is so richly but unevenly endowed." Forecasting for future generations, they now insist that the entire river system must be considered as a unit.

While Hoover Dam solved a good many of the problems of the lower Colorado basin, it did little except to provide a source of electricity for the upper basin states. In years of low flow they have very little water, particularly for irrigation. Thus the Colorado River Storage Project was born. The most impressive part of this is the Glen Canyon Dam, which is just a few feet shorter than its predecessor, and which has produced Lake Powell—according to Secretary of Interior Udall, the ultimate boss of Reclamation, a lake of "almost unbelievable beauty" in a "setting of incomparable grandeur." Dam building has come a long way since Theodore Roosevelt set out to help the farmers of Arizona grow crops, but he undoubtedly would have approved the later developments.

Other dams in the system, less spectacular but still impressive, are the Flaming Gorge in Wyoming and the Navajo in New Mexico. Still others are authorized or under construction. In the words of Secretary Udall, "Like huge barrels on the Colorado River and its main tributaries, they will catch and hold surplus water in years of high runoff."

But there is just not quite enough water in the Colorado River. The seven-state compact that divided the region into upper and lower basins gave each basin 7.5 million acre-feet of water and left 1.5 million for Mexico. A total allocation of 16.5 million acre-feet seemed ample, in view of the belief that the river's flow amounted to 20 million acre-feet annually. In recent years the flow has been between 15 and 16 million acre-feet which with evaporation is simply not enough.

To fill the Lake Powell, Flaming Gorge, and Navajo reservoirs, Lake Mead was allowed in 1965 to drop as low as it was possible for it to still generate electric power. Nevertheless Lake Powell reached only the minimum level necessary to generate the electric power that is needed to pay for the Glen Canyon Dam.

In spite of all this the states of the lower basin are now calling for new dams. Two are projected, both of them upstream from Hoover but below Glen Canyon. The first to be built will be on Marble Canyon, at the upper boundary of the Grand Canyon. The construction at Bridge Canyon, which will produce a lake thirteen miles long in the lower part of Grand Canyon (a region inaccessible except by boat) has been put off in deference to conservationists, but will possibly be built eventually.

The Bureau of Reclamation is responsible for development of water resources in the western states. Most of this area receives less than twenty inches of rain a year, not enough for regular farm production. The West does, however, have many rivers fed from melting snow on the high mountains. These mountains, a barrier to the early settlers going west, may now mean salvation to the descendants of those settlers.

Loath to see any water at all get to the sea, Westerners generally are in favor of the dam-building that continually goes on. As of 1965, the Bureau of Reclamation had completed 210 dams, and altogether they hold back enough water to bury the states of Nebraska and Kansas under a foot of water. Outside of the Colorado, the most famous of the Bureau's projects is probably the Grand Coulee Dam in Washington, one of the largest in the world, which can irrigate a million acres of land, and which at the same time produces enormous amounts of hydroelectric power. The Bureau also has major dams on the Sacramento and San Joaquin rivers in California, in the Central Valley of California, and on the Canadian River in Texas, which provides many cities with water for municipal use.

In one rather startling project, known as the Big Thompson, the Bureau transfers water from the snowy western slopes of the Rockies to their arid eastern side by means of a very long tunnel through the Colorado Continental Divide. What makes the activity unlikely is that the water is "surplus" from the Colorado River. That there really is no such surplus seems to be admitted by the Bureau's experiments with rain-making on those same western slopes.

It is impossible to talk about water in the Southwest without continually referring to the Colorado. The river even entered into international relations when the treaty with Mexico stipulated that 1.5 million acre-feet of the river must arrive below the border every year. This amount is difficult to reserve in any event, with water-hungry Los Angeles just above the border, but the difficulty has increased since Mexico began demanding fresher water. Though comparatively free from silt, thanks to the construction of the dams, Colorado water still has a high saline content owing to frequent use and re-use for irrigation on its way south. The Mexicans say they need fresher water to irrigate cotton crops on the river delta, although farmers in Yuma, just to the north, use the same salty water and say that cotton grows perfectly well. At this juncture even the State Department is drawn into the question of water supply.

The Miracle of Los Angeles

The Bureau of Reclamation asserts that almost all of the cost of construction of water resource facilities is returned to the United States Government. Hoover Dam is being paid for by the sale of electric power, a good proportion of it to the Metropolitan Water District of Southern California and notably to Los Angeles. The construction of this dam permitted southern California to undertake one of the more spectacular water projects in an area where the spectacular is almost a commonplace.

Judging by the enormous amounts of oil, which is a fossil fuel, that have been found in the area, southern California must once have been an area of lush vegetation. Later it must have been covered by the sea, a necessary development in the formation of oil. In more recent times, however, the climate has been dry and sunny, fine for the movie industry but less so for supporting a large population of car washers and lawn waterers, not to mention swimming pools. The first Spanish settlers had managed to raise cattle so long as the rainfall averaged fifteen inches a year, but a prolonged drought brought an end to cattle-raising. Later settlers used gasoline-driven pumps to draw from an extensive supply of ground water far below the surface. For a time well water was plentiful, and there were hundreds of companies in Los Angeles County to supply it. Then the inevitable happened—the water table was overdrawn.

Looking around for new supplies, city officials spotted the Owens River on the east side of the High Sierra, more than 200 miles away. After considerable difficulty with the Owens River natives, the water was brought around the mountains in an aqueduct that was opened in 1913. This, added to the sizable amount Los Angeles was still able to draw from what remained of the ground water, was adequate for a time. But the city, whose one natural river bed is now cement-lined and nearly always dry, continued to grow and so did the population of the surrounding countryside. In 1928, as water once more became scarce, a Metropolitan Water District, representing many small cities, was formed. It amounted to a monopoly, in the sense that only residents of one of the cities could draw on the water. In order to qualify, a neighboring community had to let itself be annexed. This was conscious empire-building on the part of Los Angeles, and in part explains the city's spectacular growth: water ran Los Angeles.

The Metropolitan Water District already had its eye on the Colorado River by the time Hoover Dam was under way, and in 1930 it issued a $200-million bond to build an aqueduct from the river. With the aid of the Bureau of Reclamation, Parker Dam was built below Boulder Canyon, and Lake Havasu came into existence. The aqueduct from it is an extremely impressive feat of engineering. Two hundred forty-two miles long, it brings the district a billion gallons of water a day over five mountain ranges and through hot desert country, lifting the water 1617 feet in the process. The power for this operation comes from Hoover Dam, and the system was completed in 1941.

The lure of the California climate is so strong that since the end of World War II the population of the metropolitan district has grown to 9.5 million. Since it will continue to grow at the rate of perhaps 400,000 a year, the water authorities are looking ahead. They are taking all the water they are allowed from the Colorado; and now that the Supreme Court decision may reduce that amount, they are looking to northern California, with its plentiful rain and its rivers running unchecked into the sea.

In 1960 the Metropolitan Water District, by then a practically independent body with a tendency to regard the government almost as a foreign power, made a contract with the State of California to bring in water from those northern rivers. This project, mostly on the San Joaquin and Sacramento rivers which join near San Francisco, will produce four million acre-feet of water a year, and the district will receive half of that beginning in 1971. This is the biggest water supply program ever undertaken anywhere in the world.

The guiding genius behind much of what the district has done is Joseph Jensen, a petroleum engineer, who works without pay at the Metropolitan Water Board's magnificent new building in downtown Los Angeles. Now in his seventies, Mr. Jensen has visions of the Southwest as it will be in another hundred years. Born in Utah, he finds the area the most beautiful in the world, and one with a magnificent climate. He sees no reason why anyone would want to live in the cold gray region of New England, New York, and Pennsylvania. Admitting that the water resources being brought into his area may make it too expensive for agriculture, he envisions an industrial complex, the most attractive that man and nature working together can possibly produce. A very specific item in that vision is the 2600 billion barrels of oil estimated to exist in the shale of Colorado, Wyoming, and Utah. If this can be utilized, and Mr. Jensen believes that within the next twenty-five years it can, it will take care of the needs of the United States for centuries to come. That utilization, like every other industrial process, would require vast amounts of water, more than the most optimistic supporters of the Colorado are able to promise. This leads Mr. Jensen, as it does all who concern themselves with water resources in the West, to think of the Columbia, which now discharges ten times the volume of the Colorado into the Pacific. Meanwhile, Mr. Jensen has authorized measures that will lead at least to a test plant for a nuclear-powered operation to desalt the water of the sea, and to other plants for determining the large-scale feasibility of reconverting waste water for domestic use.

California, already the most populous state, expects to have doubled its population by 1990. There are hopes that the State Water Project will take care of the supply until that date. There are already dams from one end of the state to the other, but they will all be dwarfed by a new one to be built for the State Water Project at Oroville on the Feather River. Oroville Dam, the keystone of the whole operation, will be ten feet higher than Hoover Dam, by which all others are still measured, and will create a long shoreline around what remains of the Feather River Canyon. So much for the next twenty-five years; after 1990, however, answers will have to be sought farther north.

The Pacific Northwest

North, to a Californian, means the old Oregon Territory, once a subject of dispute with Great Britain and with Russia, a territory that was split into the states of Washington and Oregon, although geographically it remains a unit. On the lands near the Pacific coast, the peaks of the Cascade Range—Baker, Rainier, Adams, Jefferson, and Hood, all over 10,000 feet high—convert the moisture, borne by the prevailing winds from the ocean, into snow and eventually into glaciers. Much of this frozen mass melts in the spring and produces disastrous floods, although the Bull Run glacier on Mount Hood supplies the city of Portland with water all year round. The plains to the east of these high mountains are in great part desert, similar to the deserts that lie in the shadow of the Sierra Nevada to the south.

At the eastern limit of the desert, the Rocky Mountains likewise trap moisture in the form of snow, and release it again as meltwater in the spring. All the rivers to the west of the Continental Divide in this area flow into the Columbia River basin. This watershed includes parts of Nevada, Utah, Wyoming, Montana, and British Columbia, as well as eastern Washington and Oregon and most of Idaho. The Snake River of Idaho is the Columbia's greatest tributary. By the time the Columbia reaches the Pacific, it is carrying more water than any other river in North America except the Mississippi.

Oregon's supply of fresh water is so rich that it can even be pumped up from wells beneath the sand dunes at the seashore. With all this moisture, forests thrive, giving Oregon its biggest industry, though the federal government owns most of the timberland and therefore exercises an exceptional degree of control over what happens in the state. The paper mills made possible by the forests also lead to one of the area's problems, namely pollution. The Willamette River, which runs through Portland, is repeatedly condemned for this reason, though the mills upstream make heroic efforts to prevent it. The mills hold the refuse in ponds until spring high water, when it can be flushed down the river, but the ponds often get too full and the waste must be sent by barge down to the Columbia. The Georgia Pacific Paper Company had a pipe that led the effluent far out to sea; but the pipe burst, and the beaches were fetid for days.

The rainfall in Oregon is not constant throughout the year; in summer it averages only a few inches. Irrigation thus becomes necessary. The worst water problem of the area, however, is floods. In spite of all the levees and dams that have been built on the Columbia and its tributaries, when melting snows are accompanied by warm rains—as happened in December 1964—the flow of water can increase by as much as ten times. The many dams that have been built, such as Bonneville, and the monumental Grand Coulee, are still not enough to make the area safe from floods.

The Columbia, which drops half a mile from its source to the ocean, is one of the world's great power streams. All of the dams along it produce electricity in addition to controlling floods. A difficulty is that the runoff is highest in spring, when the demand for power is least, and lowest in winter, when the demand is greatest. The lakes behind the dams, therefore, have the added purpose of storing water for the right time of year.

The construction of a complete system of dams on the Columbia, one that would utilize all available power and stop any conceivable flood, is hampered by the conflicting interests of those who have a say in the matter. The salmon industry opposes all dams, and must be placated; private power companies object to the building of any more public-power dams. There was considerable wrangling over the Snake River between federal agencies, whose interest was in dams that would be of use in flood control, and private companies, whose interest was only in the power the river could provide. After President Eisenhower appointed Douglas McKay, a car dealer from Washington, as Secretary of the Interior, one of the new Secretary's first acts was to settle the controversy in favor of the power companies.

The Army Corps of Engineers and the Bureau of Reclamation, both of which have had their troubles in coming to terms over the Missouri River, have conflicted so sharply over the Columbia that the governor of Oregon finally appealed to President Johnson; two approved projects were being held up by the Bureau because, in the governor's words, Reclamation was trying to get one of them away from the Engineers.

The drier states to the south have added rancor to the talk about water that regularly goes on in the states of Oregon and Washington. They seem to have the backing of Secretary Udall, who was brought up in Arizona. In response to proposals for diverting Columbia water, a Portland banker said, "The Northwest's prosperity is based entirely on the supply of fresh water. Under conditions like that, it is easy to see why some think that talk of the export of water from this section of the country is equivalent to treason." This same banker proposed that water-rich states in the Northwest band together to protect the supply from those who "envy our resource."

The governor of Washington absolutely refuses to discuss the question. The governor of Oregon received a large sum from the legislature to finance a water resources study, which will project the needs of the state to the year 2070. This will be a useful tool when the federal government moves in to settle matters on the Columbia—as must surely happen since the river is, after all, an interstate waterway. More and more people are moving to Oregon, and the possibility of irrigating the dry lands in the east has scarcely been explored. There is some grazing in the arid Valley of the Moon area, for instance, but the land there is good only, as the saying goes, "for cattle with mouths a foot wide grazing at thirty miles an hour." Looking at the steady influx of settlers, a local author wrote, "The Lord quit making land but he didn't quit making people." The governor wants to find out how much water the state could possibly use, because he doesn't want to allocate any to the Southwest and then have to fight to get it back.

One of the proposed plans for diversion would extract an amount almost equal to the annual flow of the Colorado from the Columbia at the Dalles Dam. The water would be lifted a mile and carried over the mountains by atomic power, and then carried another 1200 miles to Hoover Dam—an operation that would double the water supply of the southwestern states.

Another proposal, offered by an Oregon lumberman, would be to take the water from farther east on the river and run it through that part of the state, fertilizing the fields on the way to a vast arid basin in Nevada and California, where it would form a reservoir the size of Lake Superior. Irrigation from there would then be used to convert the dry San Joaquin Valley into lush farmland.

Still another plan would be to take the water from near the mouth, after every conceivable use had been made of it by the states that own it, and then pump it over the high Cascades, where it would be added to the system now being built to carry water from northern to southern California.

Officials in the Southwest are also taking a look at the Feather, Yellowstone, and Snake rivers. But they are not finding Idaho very cooperative, as a statement by Dr. William Folz of the University of Idaho at a Western Interstate Water

Conference suggests: "What I am saying in as polite a manner as I can is this: You wealthy states who have grandiose plans for your own future growth in wealth and population had better give serious thought to the more modest and meager aspirations of your less fortunate neighbors, for, if you don't, we will find some way literally to shut your water off."*

Meanwhile, the dam building goes on. One in Hells Canyon has the backing of the Idaho Power Company. In Washington and Oregon, the Army Engineers are trying to resettle the townspeople displaced by the new John Day Dam. In British Columbia, work has begun on the Duncan Dam, the first of three such structures on the Columbia that will sell power to the United States.

In the face of all this, it is a question just how much longer the migratory salmon will survive.

* Others in Idaho ask if the citizens are free to decide their own future, or if they must be compelled to remain a water faucet and a wild playground for the rest of the United States.

11

The Years Ahead

The Problem of Irrigation

THE man who has benefited most from the several thousand dams built by the United States Government is the farmer who depends on irrigation. This in itself is "good"; everyone, after all, wants to see the deserts bloom. In 1965 there were 128,863 farms irrigated by projects of the Bureau of Reclamation. Seven and a half million acres of such land produced fruits, vegetables, and other crops worth about $1.5 billion. Since the Bureau of Reclamation was begun in 1906 it is estimated to have made possible an agricultural production worth a total of $20 billion, out of a total federal investment of only $5 billion—much of which has already been returned to the Treasury through the sale of hydroelectric power and irrigation rights. But what sounds like an unmixed blessing may turn out, when the total needs of the United States are considered, not to be that at all.

Almost half of all the water used in the United States goes into irrigation. In California 90 per cent of it goes for that purpose. It must be repeated that such water is really used up, either by transpiration from growing plants or by evaporation from the ground. It takes 200,000 gallons to produce a ton of rayon, but that amount then goes back into the waterways. An acre of cotton simply uses up 800,000 gallons; an acre of orange or grapefruit trees uses up more than a million gallons.* In irrigation, people talk in acre-feet rather than gallons. It is being asked seriously, even in the Southwest, whether the nation can afford still greater subsidies for the farmer—already the most subsidized businessman in the United States—in terms either of money or of water supply. It is all very well to have fresh fruits and vegetables from southern California and Arizona the year round; but how much are we actually paying for them?

The irrigation process involves a fantastic degree of waste. Half the water that flows in ditches and canals is lost by seepage and evaporation. Many canals are now being lined with concrete and other watertight materials, but this adds considerably to the expense. Again, only half the water that reaches the fields is actually used by the plants. No one knows exactly how much water various kinds of crops need for ideal growth, although the Department of Agriculture has made many studies on the subject, which has developed into the new science of micrometeorology. That better use could be made of irrigation water seems clear from the experience of the farmer in the San Joaquin Valley who used a computer in order to decide how much water to use. He discovered that he was using twice the amount he needed, and is now saving $3500 a year on irrigation water bills.

A number of problems arise in the handling of water for irrigation. A considerable amount of that held in reservoirs simply evaporates. What survives the hazard of depletion on

* A hopeful development is the patent taken out by the University of Illinois for a chemical that reduces transpiration in trees and other plants, and thus significantly cuts down on their consumption of water.

the way to the fields brings with it the ancient problem of all irrigation cultures—that it deposits salts. No one yet knows what to do about that except to wash the soil by applying an excess amount of water. This in turn can raise the water table to the point where roots become waterlogged and the plants die—another unresolved ancient difficulty. Adequate drainage therefore remains a problem, particularly on flat lands. It was solved in the cultivated fields of the Imperial Valley by digging down several feet and lining the excavation with tiles—an expensive remedy that is possible only where the crop has a high market value and there is a year-round growing season.

A new problem of irrigating arid lands has led to the coining of a new word, "hydrocompaction." In the 1950s the canals that had recently been dug to bring water to virgin lands in the western San Joaquin Valley gradually began to sink, as the water seeping down into clay deposits forced out the air. One canal subsided in depth from five to twenty feet, and had to be abandoned because it was too far below the level of the lands it was designed to irrigate. Water on apparently level fields found soft pockets, which slowly sank until the area was full of hummocks. A test field that was kept continuously submerged for nineteen months sank ten feet. The only solution in such lands seems to be to speed up the compaction before planting is undertaken at all.

Irrigation may also contribute in various ways to the problem of pollution. One of these is the seepage into the ground water of the nitrates that have been applied to the soil as fertilizer, and that can cause illnesses such as anemia. It is said that in the irrigated lands of the West, the plants absorb only half of the nitrogen fertilizer, and that the rest soaks down into the underground water reservoirs. In some parts of the fertile San Joaquin Valley, contaminated drainage has already ruined good farm land. At Camp Pendleton, the

United States Marine base in California, the wells used for a water supply had to be abandoned because of contamination by fertilizer that drained from citrus groves on higher ground. At San Luis Obispo, doctors have recommended that the local hospitals use bottled water because in the local supply the concentration of nitrates has increased by 1000 per cent in the last ten years. In an effort to get rid of agricultural waste water a 200-mile drainage canal is being built from central California to San Francisco Bay. Authorities are now wondering how much worse this will make the situation in that already seriously polluted body of water. Will it ultimately affect the fishing, as the tides carry the polluted water out into the Pacific Ocean?

Quite aside from such complications, it is clear that irrigation is complex and expensive in itself. In the West, where over the years the United States government has spent $21.5 billion for water development, the farmer is charged only one-tenth to one-third of the cost. Some experts believe that irrigation in the United States has already gone about as far as it can go. Some say that the Southwest can hope to expand only by a shift from agriculture to a predominantly industrial base. This seems particularly true of Arizona, with its mushrooming cities of Phoenix and Tucson. Five billion gallons of water are pumped every day from the total underground water supply, and only half of this is being restored. Almost all of what is lost goes into irrigation. To ward off the otherwise inevitable day when Arizona's ground water is exhausted, the solution would seem to be more people and less farming. As for California, now the nation's largest producer of farm products, who knows what may be in store?

International Water Developments

Irrigation and water supply concern the United States government not only nationally but internationally. We share the Columbia, the lakes of the Minnesota wilderness, the Great Lakes, and the St. Lawrence with Canada, and the Gulf of Mexico, the Colorado, and the Rio Grande with our neighbor to the south. Each of these waters is an opportunity for development, as well as an occasion of controversy. Further afield, it has been regarded as in the national interest to lend scientific skill and a certain amount of money for water projects in developed as well as undeveloped countries.

Curiously, even rainy England is short of water. Experts believe its supply will have to be doubled in the next twenty years. The British have been building new reservoirs and are even looking into desalinization.

Israel, which will surely go to war if Syria persists in its threat to divert the Jordan River, can certainly be regarded as developed in terms of water management. It has built a vast system of irrigation canals and pipelines, and at present has three desalinization plants in operation. The United States plans to put up $50 million of the $200 million needed there to build a desalinization plant, which will use nuclear fuel, and which when completed will produce 26 million gallons of fresh water daily, as well as considerable electrical power.

The United States had planned to put up funds to help another arid country, Egypt, build a dam at Aswan, but, through the decision of Secretary of State Dulles, the plan was abandoned, a decision that has had, like so many decisions concerning water, a number of political repercussions.

Through its membership in the Food and Agriculture Organization of the United Nations, the United States participates in activities over much of the globe. One that involves water is in the Mediterranean, for thousands of years the center of Western civilization but now an area in need of redevelopment. For centuries the soil has been misused, denuded of forests, and overgrazed. As a result, food production has declined, and matters have been made worse in recent years by devastating floods. Throughout the Mediterranean, little or no rain falls during the long growing season. The plan is to make it another California. By 1980 the amount of land under irrigation will have been doubled; numerous dams will be built; vast stores of ground water that are known to exist will be brought to the surface. Much cutover land will be reforested. The Mediterranean project will cost billions, but by 1980 it will have increased the productivity of the land by as much as $10 billion a year. And it will vastly improve the lives of millions of peasants who still exist in the miserable agrarian poverty that has caused so many of their relatives to emigrate to North and South America. One of the first success stories of the project announced a threefold production increase in the irrigated lands of Greece.

Another large project of the FAO is the development of the resources of the Mekong River, which is proceeding despite the warfare in Vietnam, through which it flows. That beleaguered country is sharing twenty-three different programs with Thailand, Cambodia, and Laos, all watered by the Mekong.

Similarly, the four West African countries of Senegal, Guinea, Mali, and Mauritania are sharing in multipurpose dams on the Senegal River, which will help them to modernize their primitive methods of agriculture.

Altogether, the FAO has more than 400 different projects around the world that are related to water. They include a vast survey in Colombia that showed how the crop and animal production could be increased many times on about

30 million acres of land that had hardly been utilized at all. Another enormous project will be to harness the Paraguay River to turn a vast undeveloped area into one resembling the Tennessee Valley. Other programs are relatively modest, such as that of supplying catamaran fishing boats in Ceylon with outboard motors, with the result that the catch has multiplied ten times.

Aware of the dependence of the nations of the world on intelligent use of water for any kind of prosperity, the United Nations is also sponsoring what it calls the International Hydrological Decade. It began in 1965 and will include such activities as measuring the discharge of a river, computing the water balance of a continent, measuring the movement of a single glacier, and finding out how much water there is in all the glaciers of the world. An important part of the program will be the establishment of international hydrological stations through which all sorts of water information can be shared. This far-seeing venture, in which sixty countries are joining, should result in making available a great deal of good water needed to grow food and keep people healthy in the future. It may be more effective in keeping world peace than are the billions of dollars spent in "foreign aid."

But the negative side must not be forgotten. Secretary of the Interior Udall referred to it when he said, "If the present rate of population increase continues indefinitely, most of the crucial problems that now confront the human race will simply become insoluble." And the Department of Agriculture points out that India, which was almost self-sufficient for food during the mid-1950s, now consumes half as much of the wheat grown in the United States as the United States does itself. It adds that India is losing the capacity to feed itself and has little chance of ever doing so again.

Dr. Roger Revelle, former head of Scripps Institution, is slightly more optimistic. He points to the Indus River. The

Indus Valley is the largest irrigated region on earth, but it is silted and badly waterlogged. If sweeping measures could be taken, famine in that part of the world could be reduced, if not eliminated. The keys are water management and modern technology. The fields are too small; they are farmed by sharecroppers; the techniques date from the Middle Ages. What are needed are water districts each a million acres in size, and an end to badly managed irrigation projects. Unfortunately, the Indians and Pakistanis, who fight over the Indus, hardly seem able to cooperate on measures of this size.

Dr. Revelle also believes that the Tigris-Euphrates Valley could be restored if the soil were leached and drained, putting millions of acres back into use. He points out the possibility of such a project in relation to a current Russian plan to dam a river and made a lake five-sixths the size of Italy. It would irrigate 50 million acres of crops, and create even more pasture.

Prospects for the Future

An official in the United States, who shall otherwise be unidentified, was once heard to suggest that the ultimate solution to the water supply problems of the northeastern United States would be to divert large amounts from lakes in the Province of Ontario—and that if Canada should object, then the United States would simply have to take it over.

Canadians are perfectly aware of the interest of the United States in their water. In spite of strong political opposition, Prime Minister Pearson has been willing to discuss the matter. "The United States," he said in a televised address, "is finding that water is one of its most valuable, and becoming one of its scarcest, resources, and we have—well, we have lots of water." Exporting water, he said, "can be as important as exporting wheat or oil. This can be one of the most important developments in our history." An official inventory is being taken in Canada, which has one-sixth of the world's fresh water supply, to see how much could be spared from its two great north-flowing river systems, the Mackenzie and Nelson, or from the province of Ontario, where one acre out of every ten is under water.

The author once asked a member of the Army Corps of Engineers whether some of the water of the Mississippi couldn't be diverted to the area once called the Dust Bowl. He added, in innocence, thinking of that city's constant flood threat, "Surely New Orleans wouldn't begrudge losing part of it."

The answer came back quickly. "Indeed New Orleans would; and so would the remainder of the Mississippi Valley. The level and flow of the river determine the loadings of its vessels, the usefulness of the docks at its ports, the intakes of its water systems, the repulsion of salt-water intrusion, the availability of its beaches, its fish and wildlife ecology, its recreation, its agriculture, its temperature, its very smell—the whole civilization of the valley." The answer is an excellent summing up of the importance of water.

A new plan for Alaska is the proposal to construct a billion-dollar dam on the Yukon River's Rampart Canyon, eighty-five miles south of the Arctic Circle. It would create a lake somewhat bigger than Lake Erie, or about the size of the state of Maryland. Senator Gruening, at the time he was governor of Alaska, said that the dam was badly needed to supply hydroelectric power if Alaska were to attract industries. The Fish and Wildlife Service has replied that the dam would cut off between 200,000 and 400,000 salmon from their spawning grounds, as well as flood out the habitat of 1.5 million ducks and geese and the homes of 12,000 moose, plus mink, musk-rat, and beaver. A different kind of objection is that the large industries that such a dam would cause to grow in a remote part of Alaska would be very expensive and difficult to defend.

The dam would probably be necessary, however, if the most ambitious plan of all, the North American Water and Power Alliance, were ever carried out. The proposal originates with the Ralph M. Parsons Company (whose offices, naturally enough, are in Los Angeles); it would cost $100 billion and take thirty years to build. Water from the Yukon and two tributaries would be sent southward through a series of dams, lifts, and tunnels into a reservoir 500 miles long, which would fill a natural gorge in the Rockies that extends through British Columbia into Montana. This water would have to be lifted 2000 feet. Water from the Laird, Fraser, Peace, and Columbia rivers would be added to the reservoir. Before it began its descent, the water would have to be lifted another thousand feet, but the power generated by its fall would perhaps pay for the operation of the lifts.

The outcome of all this would be enough water to meet the needs of seven Canadian provinces, thirty-three of our own fifty states, and three of the states of Mexico. It would irrigate 40 million acres in the United States and give Mexico eight times as much new farm land as the Aswan Dam will provide in Egypt. A secondary feature would be a 2000-mile waterway, running east, that would fill up the Great Lakes and even supply water to New York City.

That there would be tremendous legal and political problems, because of the rights and interests of the many people involved, is not to be doubted, but it could be done! By now, indeed, the technology exists to do anything in the field of water supply that someone is willing to pay for. Rivers can be turned backward, water can be made to run uphill—but only at great cost. People will have to stop thinking of water as something free; and they will have to start thinking ahead ten, twenty, thirty years.

David Lilienthal, the former head of the Tennessee Valley Authority, wrote in 1965:

> With increased urbanization and industrialization, demands on the water supply will be much greater than most Americans have remotely imagined. The drought in the northeast United States last summer was an indication of shortages even greater to come. And though engineers and scientists can, and will, tap new sources of water and devise ways to purify polluted rivers like the Hudson, the cost will be fantastic—hundreds of billions of dollars. Add to the current strain the pressure of 50 per cent increase in population and the result may well be a chronic water shortage that can hardly be solved at any tolerable price.

A citizen may hope that Mr. Lilienthal is being unduly pessimistic, and that Americans can and will pay whatever the cost of adequate water amounts to. The average American family spends $3 a month for its indispensable water, whereas its phone bill is about $7.30, and its monthly expenditure for liquor is more than $15. It is possible, of course, that man's future use of water, whether in rivers and lakes or in the salty ocean, may spell the doom of the species. On the other hand, a sufficient degree of wise use may keep the race alive until the people of all nations have realized that the mindless proliferation of the species can only bring misery to all. Before it is too late, one may hope that everyone will learn one elementary fact: that there is a very definite limit to the amount of water available, and therefore a no less definite limit upon the amount of food that can be grown to keep people alive.

Suggested Reading

BASCOM, WILLARD. *Waves and Beaches.* New York: Doubleday & Co., 1964.

BRUUN, ANTON, ed. *The Galathea Deep Sea Expedition.* New York: The Macmillan Company, 1956.

CARSON, RACHEL. *The Sea Around Us* (rev. ed.). New York: Signet Science Library, 1961.

COKER, R. E. *This Great and Wide Sea.* New York: Harper & Row Torchbooks, 1962.

DAVIS, KENNETH S. and DAY, JOHN A. *Water: The Mirror of Science.* New York: Doubleday & Co., 1961.

EWING, MAURICE. "With 'Atlantis' to the Mid-Atlantic Ridge," *National Geographic Magazine,* September 1948 and November 1949.

GASKELL, T. F. *Under the Deep Oceans.* New York: W. W. Norton & Co., 1960.

HILL, MAURICE N., ed. *The Sea.* 3 vols. New York: John Wiley & Sons, 1963.

KING, THOMSON. *Water: The Miracle of Nature.* New York: The Macmillan Co., 1953.

MINER, ROY WALDO. *Field Book of Seashore Life.* New York: G. P. Putnam's Sons, 1950.

PICCARD, JACQUES and DIETZ, ROBERT S. *Seven Miles Down: The Story of the Bathyscape "Trieste."* New York: G. P. Putnam's Sons, 1961.

RAITT, HELEN. *Exploring the Deep Pacific.* New York: W. W. Norton & Co., 1964.

SPILHAUS, ATHELSTAN. *Turn to the Sea.* Racine, Wisconsin: Whitman Pub. Co., 1962.

SVERDRUP, JOHNSON, and FLEMING. *The Oceans: Their Physics, Chemistry and Biology.* New York: Prentice-Hall, Inc., 1942.

TIME, INC. *The Sea.* New York, 1961.

U.S. GOVERNMENT PRINTING OFFICE. *A Primer on Water.*

———. *A Primer on Ground Water.* Two excellent booklets put out by the Geological Survey of the Department of Interior and available from the Superintendent of Documents, Washington, D.C., 20402.

The magazine *Scientific American* has publishes many excellent articles on oceanography. Back issues are available at public libraries. Other periodicals in the field are *Oceanus,* published by the Woods Hole Oceanographic Institution, *Sea Frontiers* from the University of Miami, and *Maritimes* from the University of Rhode Island.

Index

Format by Mort Perry
Set in Linotype Baskerville
Composed, printed and bound by American Book–Stratford Press, Inc.
HARPER & ROW, PUBLISHERS, INCORPORATED